Praise

When a Woman Tells the Truth

"Glimpses of rich lives, lived long, with roots in the past but still growing towards the future: when older women tell their truth, it looks like this."
—Laurie R. King, *New York Times* bestselling author of 30 novels including *The Beekeeper's Apprentice*

"With the title from Adrienne Rich, *When a woman tells the truth she is creating the possibility for more truth around her,* the editors honor voices we need to hear: women over 80. These poets, prose writers, and artists share thoughts on how to live. Over and over, they choose art, resilience, and truth—from turning the mulch to politics to loneliness, to desire, from children to grandchildren, from re-reading books to losing words. *I have lived on the edge of despair,* writes poet Patricia Grube, *and of happiness / and sometimes / both at once.* Addressing age, inspiration, experience, sexuality, physicality, and life, this collection provides perspective and wisdom for all readers, and honors, as poet Nellie Wong says: *Remembering   living   a witness in/Story   in unhurried song.*"
—Ellen Bass, Chancellor Emerita of the Academy of American Poets, author of *Indigo*

"I found *When a Woman Tells the Truth* a cornucopia of delights that should become your new companion. This book is to be read slowly, over the years, taking time to savor the pieces one at a time. You will find joy, beauty, and wisdom throughout. It will help you make meaning out of the losses, challenges, and surprises of growing old."
—Katharine Esty, psychologist and author of *Eightysomethings: A Practical Guide to Letting Go, Aging Well and Finding Unexpected Happiness*

"Oh, when elder women tell the truth—and the women in this volume are elders—they open doors to the mostly unacknowledged wisdom of half our species.

"What's inspiring is more than their intelligence as they face health and awareness problems, it's their attitudes. And there's humor here. In the multitude of stories and poems, such variety and range of issues and strategies we all will find our so-called 'unique' personal challenges mirrored with such accuracy we'll snap to attention. We're reading what our next step might be. Or must be. We'll find ourselves examining hints of more than a handful of ways to deal. The shared feeling here, generally, is that life is still a grand adventure. And deserves our full attention.

"This book shows us women being real about life. Together they are the village elder, two hundred and fifty thousand years old, who knows everything. This is the twenty-first century version of that elder, and this book will change your life. Who needs to read it? Everyone."

—Clive Matson, author: *Let the Crazy Child Write!* and
Hello, Paradise. Paradise, Goodbye

"We hear a lot about aging these days—but rarely from the people who know it best. *When a Woman Tells the Truth* brings together the poetry, prose, and art of more than eighty women over eighty. Here are poets, professors, Zen buddhists, theater directors, French teachers, jewelry artists, union organizers, midwives, hospice workers, and more. These compelling dispatches from the land of eighty and beyond are by turns loving, funny, heartbreaking, sly, tender, and angry. Through it all, the light of great and small joys shines through, along with the fierce clarity of seeing the present, each day, for what it is."

—Kathryn Chetkovich, author of *Friendly Fire*

"This unique anthology of writing by women over 80 is a refresher course in keeping feisty, funny, and fit—despite late-life challenges to all three. From prose like Sheila Carrillo's 'No Red Diapers For Me: A Late-in-Life Encounter With Socialism', to poems like Katherine Williams'

'Afterlife', which ends: *I'm thirsty for the actual light of stars still shining eons after their end,* this wide-ranging and racy anthology belies any notion that women over 80 are too old to kick butt, dispense hard-earned truths, and make us laugh so hard we pee.

"From the ferocity of Fereshteh Fatemi's feminist rallying cry, to Maude Meehan announcing:

...did I / mention by the way that when
I heal and throw away this cane
I have on layaway a big red Harley?

"These raucous manifestos are zippy as that woman on her late-in-life Harley.

"Did I mention racy?

"Here's Susan Terris' poem 'Pubic Enemy' in its entirety:

Shave it, wax it, pluck the black coils
Escaping your bikini bottom.

Brazilian, French—the triangle, sphynx,
The landing strip, moustache, the heart.

A source of obsession. But older now,
Much much older....

Where is that burning bush?

"What a sacrilegious zinger of an ending! Catch a ride with these women. But hold on tight."

—David Allen Sullivan, author of *Black Butterflies Over Baghdad,*
Poet Laureate of Santa Cruz

When a Woman Tells the Truth

PREVIOUSLY PUBLISHED WORKS BY DENA TAYLOR

Exclamation Points: Collected Poems, Many Names Press, 2020.

Tell Me the Number before Infinity: The story of a girl with a quirky mind, an eccentric family, and oh yes, a disability, co-authored with Becky Taylor, Many Names Press, 2016.

Disabled Mothers: Stories and Scholarship by and about Mothers with Disabilities, co-edited with Gloria Filax, Demeter Press, 2014.

Red Flower: Rethinking Menstruation, Crossing Press, 1988, reprinted by The Blackburn Press, 2002.

Feminist Parenting: Struggles, Triumphs & Comic Interludes, editor, Crossing Press, 1994.

The Time of Our Lives: Women Write on Sex after 40, co-edited with Amber Sumrall, Crossing Press, 1993.

Sexual Harassment: Women Speak Out, co-edited with Amber Sumrall, Crossing Press, 1992.

Women of the 14th Moon: Writings on Menopause, co-edited with Amber Sumrall, Crossing Press, 1991.

PREVIOUSLY PUBLISHED WORKS BY
WILMA MARCUS CHANDLER

The Night Bridge: Collected Poems, Hummingbird Press, 2016.

Kiss or Kill: Contact Scenes of Love and Strife, with Steve Ramshur, Smith & Kraus, Inc., 2009.

Directing Theater 101, Smith & Kraus, Inc., 2008.

The Ultimate Scene Study Series: Scenes for Three Actors, Scenes for Four Actors, Scenes for Groups, Smith & Kraus, Inc., 2001.

8 Tens @ 8 Festival: 30 10-Minute Plays from the Santa Cruz Festivals I-VI, with John Patterson, Smith & Kraus, Inc., 2001.

When a Woman Tells the Truth

Writings and Creative Work by Women Over 80

Dena Taylor & Wilma Marcus Chandler,
Editors

Many Names Press
Blue Lake, California

First Edition.
ISBN 978-1-944497-09-5
Library of Congress Control Number: 2024937073

Kate Hitt, ManyNamesPress.com
Email: khitt@manynamespress.com
PO Box 737, Blue Lake, CA 95525 USA

Credits:
Book design: Kate Hitt
Cover design: Janet Fine
Cover art: *Looking Back* by Lynda Watson
Alice Neel *Self-Portrait* © Courtesy The Estate of Alice Neel and David Zwirner
Photos of Lynda Watson's jewelry by rrjones, photographer
Back cover photo of Dena Taylor by Maria Zamudio & Janet Fine
Back cover photo of Wilma Marcus Chandler by Jana Marcus

The front cover features Lynda Watson's jewelry piece entitled *Looking Back,* about which she says:

We delve into the past precisely so that we can feel grounded enough to face up to the challenges of the present. In anchoring us in our own history, nostalgia helps to create a consistent sense of identity, which is the stabilizing force we need to face problems—whether personal or global.

I decided that I would challenge myself to make a piece to wear to the opening reception of my Master Metalsmith Exhibition—and that it should most fittingly be a retrospective piece. Since my work is always about my life, it seemed appropriate to use details from existing pieces that are about the memorable events and times I've experienced and some of the places that I've been over the last fifty-plus years.

Dedication

To our mothers, Anne Taylor (1919-2001) and
Jacqueline Kantrowich (1909-1999), in memoriam,
who would have loved to read this collection of poems and
stories, and would no doubt have added their two cents!
And to Judy Reynolds, who was the inspiration
for this book.

Acknowledgments

Deep thanks and appreciation to Janet Fine for designing the cover and for her assistance with the artwork.

We are grateful for the help of our daughters Becky Taylor, Anna Taylor, Jana Marcus, and Valerie Marcus Ramshur for all their suggestions and support, and to Topsy Smalley and Lynne Alper for their research.

We stand in awe of all the women who sent work to us, including those whose pieces we were not able to use, for their honesty in writing about their lives.

And lastly, hats off to our publisher and book artist-poet Kate Hitt of Many Names Press for her enthusiasm and expertise in producing this anthology.

Table of Contents

Introduction
Page xxi

How It Is Now

The Wide World

What Inspires

~The Arts~

~Nature~

~The Political World~

How I Got Here

Sexuality, Romance, Love

The Body

Circle of Life

Women's Wisdom

Contributors' Biographies
Page xxix

Previously Published Authors' Works
Page xlix

Recommended Reading & Resources
Page li

Introduction

The idea for this book came about as friends sat around discussing what it meant to be turning 80, wondering what other women felt, what their lives were like. A couple of us had the idea of collecting accounts and putting together a book. So off went calls for submissions in various literary sources, and we were amazed at the response. Women in their 80s and 90s from all over the country and abroad sent us stories about their joys, sorrows, adventures, love lives, losses, memories, and their aches and pains. There was sadness. There was humor. There was advice. There was so much! And we received artwork as well, some of which is included.

The title, *When a Woman Tells the Truth,* is part of a quote by the writer Adrienne Rich. The full sentence is "When a woman tells the truth she is creating the possibility for more truth around her." It is in her landmark book *On Lies, Secrets, and Silence,* published by W.W. Norton & Co., 1979.

Women over 80 have done and are doing important, beautiful, and amazing things. We've cited just some of them here, but this is by no means a complete list.

Mary Ross of the Cherokee Nation—scientist, mathematician, astronomer, and the first Native American woman to be an engineer—was a pioneering figure of the space age. She dedicated her retirement years, into her 90s, encouraging young women and Native American youth to enter careers in math, science, and engineering. She died in 2008 just short of her 100th birthday.

Dolores Huerta, at 94, continues to champion the rights of farm workers. Dame Ivy Dumont, now in her 90s, was the seventh governor-general of the Bahamas, where she was the first woman to hold this office. After leaving public service, Dumont wrote her autobiography and remained active, speaking in public schools and encouraging youth to further their education.

Congresswoman Maxine Moore Waters, 85, has represented California's 43rd congressional district since 1991. Nancy Pelosi, 83, served as the 52nd speaker of the United States House of Representatives from 2007 to 2011 and again from 2019 to 2023. At 90, Dianne Feinstein, "a California legend," was the longest-serving woman senator in U.S. history.

In her 80s, Mother Jones was still traveling across the country in support of workers' struggles. Also, into her 80s, abolitionist and social activist Harriet Tubman worked with the home she established for aged and indigent African Americans.

Colette Maze is a French pianist. In 2023, at age 109, she released her seventh album, making her one of the oldest recording pianists in the world. The four Bonnema sisters from Prinsburg, Minnesota, are all in their 80s and continue to give piano recitals. Marlene Sai, 81, is still singing in Hawaii. Angela Alvarez won "best new artist" at the Latin Grammys at 95, and Mavis Staples and Judy Collins continue to perform.

Lena Horne, American singer, actress, dancer, and civil rights activist, was still performing and recording in her 80s. She is the first Black woman to have a Broadway theater named after her.

Both Joan Baez and Buffy St. Marie, after decades-long singing careers, are now doing humanitarian work and writing books, making the world a better place. Singer Carole King is politically active in her 80s, going to Washington to get support for environmental issues.

Actresses over 80 who continue to perform in film and onstage include Jane Fonda (who is still very politically active), Lily Tomlin, Rita Moreno, Vanessa Redgrave, Carol Burnett, and Glenda Jackson. In her 80s, Jackson returned to Broadway in a revival of Edward Albee's *Three Tall Women,* winning the 2018 Tony Award for Best Actress in a Play. After that, she continued to perform on Broadway and on TV.

Ida Vitale, 99, is a Uruguayan poet, translator, essayist, lecturer, and literary critic. She published four books and won several literary awards after age 80. Ten years ago, four Ventura County women in their late 80s and 90s were honored as literary treasures for the writing they had done and were still doing.

Ruth Stone was an American poet who catapulted to fame at 87 when she won the National Book Award for her collection *In the Next Galaxy.* A spate of honors followed this award. In 2007, she was named poet laureate of Vermont. Two years later, her volume *What Love Comes To* was a finalist for the Pulitzer Prize in poetry.

German-born British writer and illustrator Judith Kerr received The Order of the British Empire award at 89 for her services to children's literature and Holocaust education. After writing more than 30 books throughout her long career, she finished her very last book, *The Curse of the School Rabbit*, just before she died at age 95. Her semi-autobiographical book, *When Hitler Stole Pink Rabbit*, gave a child's-eye view of escaping Hitler's persecution of Jews.

83-year-old Holocaust survivor Henia "Henny" Lewin speaks to school children about her life. "I hope I have an impact. I want to connect with them and let them know how important it is to be an activist. If I can connect with just one, I feel like I've had an impact," she said. And Gitta Ryle, whose work is in this anthology, affirms these beliefs.

There are women in their 90s and older who run races. 100-year-old Diane "Flash" Friedman did the 100- and 200-meter dashes, followed by the javelin, at the Michigan Senior Olympics Track and Field Meet in August 2021. As Diane is often heard telling others, "Keep moving!!" Harriette Thompson, who died in 2017, was an American classical pianist who later held the record for the oldest woman to run a marathon, at age 92, and the oldest woman to complete a half-marathon, at 94.

Shirley Goodman, known as "The Dancing Nana," is 100 years old. "I feel great —100 is just a number to me," she says. In 2011, Eileen Ash became the first female test cricketer to live to 100. At 105, she did yoga weekly and lived to be 110.

Judy Smith of Boston achieved the #1 ranking in the 80 and over International Tennis Federation's World Senior Championship in Umag, Croatia. "To have this chance at the age of 80, for the first time, was beyond thrilling!" And she's still competing at age 88!

Anthropologist Jane Goodall, the world's foremost expert on chimpanzees, was still on the board of the Nonhuman Rights Project at age 88. Mary Quant, British fashion designer, published *My Autobiography* when she was 89. Martha Stewart, at 81, was on the cover of *Sports Illustrated* in a swimsuit.

101-year-old Iris Apfel was an American businesswoman, interior designer, and fashion icon. At 90, she became a visiting professor at the University of Texas at Austin. At 95 she performed in a television commercial for a French automobile and was also the face of Australian brand Blue Illusion. At 97 she published a biography with HarperCollins entitled *Iris Apfel: Accidental Icon,* and she signed a modelling contract with global agency IMG.

Two friends in their 80s, Ellie Hamby and Sandy Hazelip, are traveling around the world, posting their adventures on social media. The Flying Octogenarians includes women pilots who are still enjoying the wonder of being in the air. Arty Trost, at 80, is circumnavigating the country, piloting her own plane.

Madhur Jaffrey, 90, is recognized for bringing Indian cuisine to the western hemisphere. Her two latest cookbooks were published in her 80s. In her early 80s she was honored for her services to cultural relations between the United Kingdom, India, and the United States, through her achievements in film, television, and cookery, and at 85 was in a rap music video. Her first cookbook, *An Invitation to Indian Cooking,* came out in 1973; it was re-released in 2023 to commemorate the 50th anniversary of its publication.

Gladys West, 92, comes from an African American farming family. She is known for her contributions to mathematical modeling of the shape of the Earth. Her work on the development of satellite geodesy models was later incorporated into the Global Positioning System (GPS), for which she was awarded the Webby Lifetime Achievement Award. She was inducted into the United States Air Force Hall of Fame in 2018. In her later years, West continued to speak to elementary students about the importance of studying science, technology, engineering, and mathematics.

Phyllis Menard lived a life of commitment to social justice and liberation movements. She moved to Santa Cruz, CA, for the final decade of her 93 years where she was involved with the Women's International League for Peace and Freedom and the Palestinian Justice Coalition.

Jean Rhys, British novelist, continued to write well into her 80s. Born on the Caribbean island of Dominica, she lived her later years in Devon, which she once described as "a dull spot which even drink can't enliven much." Another British author, A.S. Byatt, had her last book published at 85.

Lebanese American writer and painter Etel Adnan was called "arguably the most celebrated and accomplished Arab American author writing today." She was still writing in her 80s and died in 2021. She was a winner of the Lambda Literary Award for Lesbian Poetry and the California Book Award for Poetry. Her artwork is shown in museums around the world.

Finnish artist and writer Tove Jansson, who wrote the Moomin children's books, continued to write into her 80s, publishing a book about her years living on an island with her life partner, the artist known as Tooti.

Annie Ernaux was awarded the 2022 Nobel Prize in Literature at 82. Isabel Allende, Barbara Maitra, Hilma Wolitzer, Cynthia Ozick, Judith Viorst, and Judy Blume are just a few of the women over 80 who continue to write. Toni Morrison was still publishing after age 80.

African American artist Betye Saar is 97, continuing to work well into her 90s. And artists Georgia O'Keeffe, Alice Neel, Agnes Martin, Mary Cassatt, Helen Frankenthaler, Leonora Carrington, Judy Chicago, Grandma Moses, Yayoi Kusama, Faith Ringgold, Hilma af Klint, and many others continued to paint in their 80s.

Maria Telkes was a Hungarian-American biophysicist and inventor who worked on solar energy technologies. She was recognized many times for her work, and at age 81 she helped the US Department of Energy to develop and build the first fully solar-powered home.

Elsie Eiler, 88, is the mayor, treasurer, clerk, secretary, librarian, and the only resident of Monowi, Nebraska. She has run the Monowi Tavern for over 50 years.

Betty Reid Soskin became a park ranger at 85, retiring at 100. And 93-year-old Joy Ryan visited every U.S. national park with her grandson, becoming stronger along the way.

But then there's this wonderful thought from a dear friend, Julie Olsen Edwards. "This is all very well," she said. "But I don't want to jump out of airplanes or be on any more committees. I'm glad women are doing these things, but I'm tired, I've worked hard, I want to take it easy now. And I don't want to feel guilty about it! The 80s truly are a different time."

The 80s—and beyond—are a different time indeed. A time for rest, reflection, doing new things, for grief, adventures, and activism. It's all here in this book. And you'll want to check out the impressive bios of the women who have contributed, who have told their truth.

Part One

How It Is Now

I like living. I have sometimes been wildly, despairingly, acutely miserable, racked with sorrow, but through it all I still know quite certainly that just to be alive is a grand thing. I live on borrowed time, waiting in the ante-room for the summons that will inevitably come. And then—I go on to the next thing, whatever it is. One doesn't, luckily, have to bother about that.
—Agatha Christie, 1890-1976
British mystery writer and playwright.

Trust your happiness and the richness of your life at this moment.
It is as true and as much yours as anything else that ever happened to you.
—Katherine Anne Porter, 1890-1980
American journalist, essayist, short story writer,
novelist, poet, and political activist.

You have to have confidence in your ability,
and then be tough enough to follow through.
—Rosalynn Carter, 1927-2023
Former First Lady of the United States.

Women have the right to say:
this is surface, this falsifies reality, this degrades.
—Tillie Olsen, 1912-2007
American feminist writer and activist.

ON THE WAY UP TO BINGHAMTON
MARIA MAZZIOTTI GILLAN

I drive up 17 West and some devil of the road
has decided to close
all lanes but one
and put up cement barriers
to the left side of the only open lane.
My driving has been getting worse and worse
although my son tells me it's always been bad.
So if you see my little red car on the road,
you should get out of the way.
When did I stop being able to drive
in a straight line? Luckily, the car beeps at me
every time I weave out of my lane,
but only one lane now remains,
I am terrified of the white cement barriers.
I am concentrating so hard and trying to avoid
hitting the barriers. I am frozen into position.
I'd like to call up the person
who decided to close all but one lane
for so many miles and ask why
he'd do such a thing, love to,
but of course I can't. I want to get past
what feels like an obstacle course
before the tractor trailers now crawling behind me,
the ones that keep beeping their horns at me,
decide to force me off the road.
I always love driving through the Catskills,
love the colors of the seasons draped over the trees.
But today I can't see them.
I'm too busy hoping I will actually reach Binghamton
without killing myself.
I think of my son telling me *if something happens to you
it will be Jennifer's problem.*

1

I explained to Jennifer that I'd rather die in motion
than die playing it safe. On Sunday I leave for Michigan
for Detroit and Grand Rapids
where I will read and teach workshops and give talks on poetry.
after the trip to Newark airport,
after the plane ride to Detroit,
after the reading at Wayne State,
after the reading at the Detroit Cultural Center,
after the two hour ride to Grand Rapids,
after the readings and talks and workshops,
after the two hour ride back to Detroit,
after the plane ride to New Jersey,
after the car ride back to my house,
I know I will need to rest,
but I know also that I will be happy
about the people who want me to sign their books
and the people who want to tell me their stories
and the way, when I get on the stage, I am suddenly
young again, grateful to be alive,
my blood pounding in my veins,
my heart singing its own wild exuberant song.

DETERMINING MY LIFESPAN AT 85
JILL GINGHOFER

A 2-for-the-price-of-one sale
Two huge bottles of Dove Shampoo.

Once home I find I already have one in use
another waiting in storage.

It takes me a year to get through one bottle.
Now I'm going to have to live at least 3-1/2 more years

which pleases me immensely,
and I refuse to consider

any of my heirs who might have benefited
from 3-1/2 bottles of Dove Shampoo.

Birthday Poem, 2020
Florence Weinberger

There must be something I can say besides
eighty-eight, let me think; I'm eighty-eight, mmm
haven't done much, haven't got much to say, or
how do you say *wonder* twenty times.
I'm strangely happy not to have done anything today
except eat dumplings and miss the movie I was going to see
because we got the time wrong and wouldn't go in
once the movie started. I came home to a few
greetings, a mangled text from my son-in-law Kenny
which came out Candy and gave me a mild chuckle.
Getting here was fraught, you know, the last few days
not sure I was going to make it, though I felt fine,
a slight sniffle. Not sure when the anxiety will start up
again, I don't want to die while Trump is still president,
probably will want to if he's reelected, and I'm not sure how
to get what I want. I was never sure how to get
what I want, but somehow got great kids and grandkids,
some poems published and splayed out on the internet, and
desire. I still have what Stanley Kunitz had, desire.
He also had roses, and my roses look like shit;
my desire is to have someone else take care of them
so I can cut them and bring them into my house,
put them into the pitcher my grandson Zane made for me,
with its curled handle, its cobalt drips and clever glazes,
and get a good night's sleep.

ON MY BIRTHDAY
ANN HOWELLS

Today, I am the oldest I have ever been,
perhaps, the wisest.
Today I drink green tea with jasmine
on my patio—
tessellated brick I laid myself,
digging the twelve-foot square,
adding sand, leveling,
placing each brick in herringbone pattern.
My hands are rough, body timeworn,
but my mind is sharp.
I sit here mornings
accompanied by birdsong, dragonfly ballet,
dog's slight nasal snore.
Every day from now on is lagniappe.

2020 Vision
Dena Taylor

Everything stopped around my birthday,
celebrated on FaceTime with whiskey and friends
There was the memorial I missed in Eugene,
a dear friend from the '60s
and two graduations in Santa Fe—

A daughter getting her Master's
A grandson finishing high school
What might his generation do
to forge a new world—
healthcare, housing, justice for all

Zoom is our connection now
Hiking group, writing group, family every Sunday
friends in England, yoga, concerts and cocktails

I buy soy creamer for my neighbor
She gives me fresh eggs
which I use in the crepes
made from sourdough starter
that we have with blueberries
nearly every morning

There've been mix-ups with the vegetable deliveries,
strange technical difficulties with phone and computer
and some animal dancing on the roof at night

I've had two ticks on my back
two crowns off my teeth
Haven't seen my lover in months
and now he has prostate cancer

Every morning my daughter and I do the *NYT* crossword
and discuss how we would answer the advice column
We find tiny yellow flowers never before noticed
on daily walks to fetch newspaper and mail
wearing whatever, no bra, wild hair
At night we watch Rachel to keep informed
then Colbert, Trevor Noah, and movies

I weed-whack and stack firewood
publish monthly newsletters for state retirees
shop every two weeks during senior hour
work on my book of poems
worry about what's next

I Want to Be 80 Forever
Julianne Johnson

Were you like me? A teen in the mid-50s? Twirling with Alice-Lon net petticoats as I jitter-bugged to Rock Around the Clock? Dashing from an after-school club meeting to a talent show rehearsal to a Pep Club section in the high school football stadium on Friday nights? Movies, dances, summer picnics at the beach. Ski boat adventures at the nearby lake. Roaming the vast sand dunes in a home-made, stripped-down sand buggy? Volunteer for special banquets. Volunteer Red Cross swim instructor at the public pool. Slumber parties in an attic, at the beach cabin, in the backyard. Staying up all night whispering secrets and giggling loud enough to get the repeated shout out from a parent to "quiet down and go to sleep."

Eighty feels the same way. Twirling from one memorable and fun invitation to the next. As my niece Becky said as a small child, we should "enjoy every crumb of every minute of every day." That describes AT EIGHTY for me.

Part of the go-go-go at this age is fueled by a keen awareness of "if not now, when?" Will there be a next time?

The year was packed with a lot of planned gallivanting. Three months in Marseilles where I walked 3-5 miles daily and earned an intermediate level in my French! Swam laps in a marvelous pool three times a week.

Then, a week in Santa Cruz to celebrate the 50th birthday of that "every crumb" author and a week in my hometown on the South Oregon Coast where my classmates—some on walkers and in wheelchairs, others still hiking—met for a day-long picnic of telling stories (lies?), reminiscing, and laughing.

One bonus of this healthy, long-lived life is reconnecting with high school and childhood friends. While we knew where so-and-so was, we had no time, what with work and kids and partners, to enrich our friendships for years and years. Now we have time as we did when we were teenagers. I'm always surprised by the call that invites me to drive an hour or so for lunch with a schoolmate or that comes from someone who has just arrived in my beach town eager for a visit. It is so easy to fall back into that trusted and vulnerable friendship where you can reminisce, ask questions and be asked, be honest and open and hoot and holler about a particular memory of a crazy time in our shared youth. It is a richness in this tapestry of life that I was not expecting. This is the benefit.

The cost? Witnessing and feeling the loss of so many whom we outlive. Sometimes the news has a meager impact: Yes, that is part of being alive. Sometimes the news knocks me flat.

Here are my antidotes: yoga, long beach walks, hikes, bicycling, lap swimming. In between, laze around, read a lot of books, and count my list of chores-to-do.

Playing with the grandgirls, ages 8 and 5, gets in the way of getting chores done. When they stay with me at the beach between Christmas and New Years, they are human alarm clocks—crawling into my bed for extra snuggles each morning. Then, I'm full-on: pool time, baking, juicing fruit, sewing monkey dolls from socks, decorating cookies, splashing in creeks that rush to the ocean, sand in every seam and pocket. I'm so grateful when 7:30pm rolls around and we can slow down and get ready for bed. They snuggle into their beds. I crash into mine. It takes me about a week to recover! But I want to be 80 forever.

I want to enjoy "every crumb of every minute of every day." I want to live my life in full bloom.

A Posthumous Compilation of Stories about Being 80
Ellen Treen

"Ahem, ah-ahem."

It takes a few hems and haws before I realize someone on the other side of the fence is trying to get my attention, but bent low over a large pot of cymbidium, searching for buds, I have been oblivious. It is unlikely I will find any this early in November, but still I look. Hanging onto the fence I straighten up, one stiff vertebrae at a time, and see Audrey, standing between her recycling bin and a bush of shaggy pink roses. Wearing that big smile of hers, she leans forward, eager for an answer to her question.

"Did you have a good birthday?"

It was only a few weeks ago, but already it seems far in the past.

"Very quiet. Most people see eighty as a mighty milestone so there was talk of a party, but it came to nothing. I was more in a contemplative than celebratory mood."

Audrey nods thoughtfully; she will get there in a few weeks herself.

"If you're wondering, I don't feel any different than I did at seventy-nine. Other birthdays were more of an event."

"Forty was the big one for me. Big and bad. Eighty is twice that." Audrey slowly shakes her head. "Some days, lately, I'm not quite here."

"You're looking great," I say, underlining great. "Really great."

"So do you. No one would guess your age."

"How many times have you heard that?" I ask, unable to stifle a sardonic scoff.

"Enough to make me wonder what eighty looks like to most people."

"People were always complimenting my mother on her youthful looks. It made her crazy. 'What's the point of looking young,' she'd mutter, 'if I can't be young?' But then she never quit trying to look younger than she was."

"When can we relax and quit fussing about how we look?"

"Who's looking?"

As though we can't help it, we appraise each other. I can hardly believe I'm wondering if Audrey looks better than I do.

"There should be a competition for octogenarians," she suggests.

"Miss Eighty wins a face-lift and double discount coupons."

"A day at the local spa."

"Prizes for who has the most teeth, or the best bridge work, or looks classy in support hose!"

I nod agreeably while wondering how crazy is it that Audrey and I should end up here in California, living in twin houses separated by a crumbling wooden fence. That we were born in the same year, in adjoining Midwestern states, each divorced after one long marriage and arrived in this small city on the West Coast. Perhaps it's crazy, perhaps it's a common story. Maybe this town is full of women turning eighty who have the same kind of stories to tell.

Audrey's daughter Miranda drives up, pops the trunk and unloads several brown bags. She has always been a frequent visitor but lately she comes by almost daily. Audrey hurries to the car and reaches for a bag.

"Mom! Let me do this."

"I can carry a bag," Audrey insists. "That's something I can do."

Hearing that controlled fury and frustration, sounds that are all too familiar, I cringe. Grabbing my green yard-waste bin, I roll it to the driveway and am filling it with clippings when I notice Audrey has joined me. Up close I can see the trembling is worse, affecting her face and jaw. Leaning on my bin as easily as she does on her own, she asks about my daughter and me.

I tell her we both had colds but we're fine. "And you?" I ask.

"Not so good." Closing her eyes, she seems to take an inward pulse. "The Parkinson's has taken another step downward." She lowers one hand in a series of stair steps, then opens her eyes.

I tell her how sorry I am and ask if there is anything that can be done.

"Another pill, I suppose," she says wearily. "Right now I'm taking Valium, which actually adds to the problem, but I was so panicked, so worried, so puzzled. Everything was going wrong. My balance was off. I had trouble eating and sleeping. And dizzy! It's not just my body, it's my brain. It's so full of holes it rattles." As though to prove her point, she shakes her head so hard I expect her teeth to loosen. "I'm not who I used to be. Nothing makes me who I used to be."

"I understand," I say ruefully. "My pills make me feel like someone else, too. But what can we do? What's the answer?"

"DEATH!" Audrey says in a near shout, and then recoils in horror.

"Eventually, of course." I speak quickly, calmly, trying to blunt the shock. "The problem is what to do during the last lap."

The sudden slam of a car trunk makes us both stiffen; we watch Miranda take a final load inside and continue to stare, even after she has disappeared. Audrey groans, "That's the worst part, the kids."

"And the best," I say promptly, and promptly feel like a Pollyanna. "We're lucky our kids are close and willing to help," I add in limp explanation, but Audrey follows her own thoughts.

"She just doesn't understand." Her voice is low and confidential. "I have Parkinson's. A disease. I'm not incompetent or an idiot. I haven't become her child." She exhales slowly, deeply. "At least not yet."

"It's tricky," I say. "I remember my mother complaining that no one gave her the kind of help she wanted. Which was to live her life the way she was used to living it, not as an invalid."

"Exactly! Sometimes I feel as though I'm under surveillance. The way they ask what I'm doing and why."

"No privacy. No dignity. They think they should know all your secrets because you require help with some things."

"Miranda is inside putting everything away. I won't be able to find the coffee for a week."

She seems so close to tears I hurry to change the subject by pointing to my bags of books, explaining, "I'm making the rounds of the used bookstores."

"I should do that," Audrey says. "But it's hard to part with books."

"I have a stack like this on my night table," Audrey says, holding her hand level with her chest. "All of them have markers showing how far I got."

"You could be describing my night table," I say. "If we have another earthquake they'll tumble down and pin me to my bed while the house collapses around me."

While I'm talking Audrey is eyeing the lumpy bags, a slightly covetous expression narrowing her eyes.

"What kinds of books do you like to read?" I ask, thinking how much easier it would be to pass my books over the fence than to lug them to stores.

"History. Some politics. Biography. Particularly autobiography. I took a class once on writing your own life story, but I didn't get too far."

"Really? I tried that too. I got as far as high school, I think."

"Do you write?" Audrey asks, in a burst of interest that almost propels her over the fence.

Without thinking I slap my hand over my mouth, swallow an internal 'whoops.' "A little," I say, shrugging dismissively.

"What do you write?" she asks.

"I keep a journal," I tell her. "Take a class, now and then. You know…"

Again, I shrug. Writing is not a subject I want to discuss with Audrey, since many of my stories are about her. "But I hardly have time right now. A friend lent me a book on feng shui. It tells you how to get rid of your clutter."

"Feng shui," Audrey frowns as she undergoes a memory search. "I thought that was about arranging furniture."

"That's part of it. You start with ditching the clutter. Last week it was old clothes. This week it's books. Feng shui has shown me the way!"

"I should get that book," Audrey says. "If I cleaned out some stuff I might get back to my writing. I get distracted by things I think I should do. That's probably what makes my life so dull."

"Audrey," I say, taking a step closer to the fence, looking her in the eye. "I doubt you or your life is dull. I bet it's more interesting than you would ever guess."

"Who would want to read it?"

"Me, for one. You can't imagine how interested I would be."

Thinking this over, Audrey's skeptical expression brightens into an engaging smile.

"I guess we do have a lot in common, don't we?"

Trying to hide my surprise, I nod agreeably while I wonder: what does she mean? Twenty-year marriages that ended in divorce, or two grown daughters. Maybe she's thinking of Ohio, where we raised small children, or our piled up night tables. Perhaps an undeniable fear of falling. Or simply the problems of women and aging.

Or something else?

I decide not to ask.

Down-Sizing While Ascending
Bonita Anne Mugnani

I'm now 83, and my To-Do list isn't any shorter than when I turned 79 and proclaimed, "It's time to Down-Size!"

It's even longer.

It seems like a tedious job, an unwelcome chore, never-ending nonsense to go through everything I've collected and gathered over all these years – to decide and determine what I'm going to keep to rekindle fond memories; let go of, in generosity of spirit, for others to appreciate and enjoy; and tenderly pack away in treasure boxes for family and friends, so as not to be forgotten.

It seems like a waste of precious time, to lose and find myself over and over again in the past, when I'm still learning so much about myself and loved ones and Life while living in the Present.

And isn't 8 the number of Infinity? Aren't my 80s supposed to be about balancing and fine-tuning that which is finite and personal while living into eternity, releasing my soul, and enlightening my spirit toward the Great Illumination? Getting ready for my death, transition, passing, departure so I can truly experience, once and for all "The Ultimate Orgasm!"

I have more important things to do!

Hmmm, what's in this dusty container? Ah, the gold satin corset and white top hat I wore at Mardi Gras as Madam Mystic, dancing behind the jazz band with the French Quarter Madams when I was 77. I can't let go of this, or this, or even these other props and costume bits I'm finding as I dig deeper, even though a picture is worth a thousand boxes. What's in that file? Oh, all the essays, stories, and poems I've written since I was 14. Those are definitely keepers. How can I get rid of this collection of blank diaries and journals? What if I'm inspired to fill them? Life isn't over yet!

Well, at least I get a lot of explorative existential thinking done as I sit here and sort. Enough is enough, though. I'm going to call some friends, go out into the twilight, listen to some live jazz, and dance my buns off!

Time is of the essence!

STEERING THE EIGHTIES
JOYCE KIEFER

Mary Lou, Sandy, and I sit down at the table in Mary Lou's apartment at her senior residence. Sandy tears open the bag of Cheetos she brought, and we begin to munch, licking the orange dye off our fingers. She knew Mary Lou would never find them in the healthy contents of the lunch box dropped at her door by the residence service.

The three of us are in our 80s—Sandy and I in the middle of the decade, Mary Lou on the far side. The conversation begins.

Mary Lou says, "You know that day trip to the coast I said I might sign up for? Well, I went and I got talking to this man and at the end he asked if I'd like to go out." She looks expectantly for reaction. She's been a widow for two years.

Sandy and I, also widows, suck in her news. We could ask what's he like, does he seem like fun, does she want to get to know him better—questions like that. But what do we ask, almost in chorus?

"Does he drive?"

"Yes!" she exclaims.

We tell her, "He sounds like a catch."

Mary Lou doesn't drive anymore, and Sandy doesn't drive at night. They don't have the freedom to jump in the car and take themselves wherever they want and go.

I've wanted to get behind the wheel since I was a kid. I got my license as a teenager; it was my ticket to independence. And it still is. I find this newly appreciated joy makes my 80s feel like my teens in reverse. I'm determined to keep driving to the museums in San Francisco, to go up to Sonoma County for an annual visit with friends, to go over the hill to Half Moon Bay, or drive up to Palo Alto to walk the stately neighborhoods when they're in spring bloom.

And I want to keep driving the 125 miles to Sacramento to meet a college classmate and then go on in his van to his family condo at Tahoe for a week or so at a time. Yes, I said *his*. Enroute, we volley ideas for the political column he continues to write for a major newspaper. Every morning we go out on his motorboat. We reach the middle of the lake, and he cuts the motor. We drift quietly, enjoying our own silence. We've each been happily married and treasure a loving family. No need for anything more in our emotional lives. I don't want it any other way, I tell others. My friend seems content with things as they are.

Mary Lou, Sandy, and I are part of a group of nine women who call ourselves "Ladies Night Out" or LNO for short. Only one of us still has a husband. We used to get together every month for 5 o'clock wine, appetizers, and dessert. "Cut to the good stuff," we'd laugh. But some of us stopped driving and the rest don't like to drive at night, so now we take turns hosting a potluck lunch. We've got to change our name, but "Ladies lunch out" lacks cachet. Over the past couple of years our gals have taken falls, had surgery, had cancer, even moved out of the area. And yet we manage to come together about every couple of months, laugh and exchange family news and health reports, and savor every minute together.

Statistics tell me the end of the road is in sight, although I notice that the Hallmark Shop carries a variety of 100th birthday cards. I wouldn't mind living long enough to receive one if I can be like my daughter's grandfather-in-law. He celebrated his hundredth with a martini and at 106 still reads the *New York Times*.

My faith tells me my spirit will continue past the grave, so I don't anticipate a yawning pit of nothingness ahead.

But what happens when I can no longer drive?

When life tightens up, I hope the joy from good moments with friendship and family will expand to fill my sense of well-being, as well as the joys that come from whichever five senses still work. I hope to delight in the sight of my garden painted silver by a full moon, the smoothness of a fresh peach, the scent of wild roses along a path on a warm day, and the taste of dark chocolate that's dark enough.

ALL IN CAPS
ELIZABETH RIVERS

It seemed simple. I'd get fruits and vegetables,
you'd get gas. We'd meet back on this curb

in fifteen minutes. But I screwed up. I was so
tired I sat down at a pillar, back-pack

on hot cement. Onions and oranges
nudging my legs—melon and cukes—

You couldn't find me in your empty mirrors.
You'd parked and hoped I 'd come to you.

Usually no one speaks to me but when
I stood up someone said, "Be careful!" I felt

thirsty, anxious, wondered how bad I looked.
I leaned on the pillar, scanned the cars.

Maybe you'd stopped searching. Your new sedan
was strange to me. It seemed everywhere

and anywhere in the vast lot. How hot
it was! What should I do? I could walk home,

or try, but if I left, how would you know?
We won't do this again. Next time I'll learn

the license plate. Next time, I'll bring a water
bottle. Wear the damn hearing aids. A rose.

Next time I'll be more careful, stronger,
wave a sign. My name. All in caps.

Self portrait by Simone Renaud

HIGH ACHIEVERS
JACKIE ZOLLO BROOKS

Sometimes everything seems dirty to me.
I rush about cleaning, doing loads of laundry
as if I still had kids,
cleaning in the corners where hairy dust
clusters imply I am lax.
I change beds in the playroom,
plump up pillows, put tinker toys away
in their faded, cracked blue box
and even wipe their tv screen, the cloth
comes back completely black.
That's how I know that everything is dirty.

At other times I work at what I call my work.
And if everything is dirty, I don't care.
I'm not looking now for cleanliness, I'm looking deep,
deeper than dust
deeper than a dryer packed with sheets
deeper than pillows dented by damp and curly heads
deeper than grandchildren in their sleep.
That's how deep I go to find what I am looking for.

—and then I dive!
not cautiously, taking a deep breath,
on the lookout for rocks where like an egg
my head would crack, no.
I defy the air, I invite the pain.
I dive, I live, I breathe
but I don't know I do these things until I've finished
writing for the day.

I feel just like my mother when she'd cleaned the house,
ironed all the clothes and stacked them on the ironing board
before putting them away. Then she'd stop to have her tea.
She might have tied her hair up in a towel,
a regular Lana Turner sitting at our kitchen table,
holding her teacup in both hands surveying all she'd done.
And then she'd say "This probably doesn't look like much
to you but I've accomplished miracles today."

TRANSITION
DENA TAYLOR

It was wrenching to leave the house,
deep in the redwoods, made of redwood.
My parents' place, at the end of the road,
built by them fifty years ago, so unique.
The two-story bookcase with a hidden ladder,
the pull-out table and wrought-iron staircase.
And buried under the tile floor near the fireplace,
a time capsule with family photos,
my two-page history of the world, and a joint.
Was I deserting it? Their dream?
Dad died first, then Ma, at 81, and I moved in.
Twenty-one years of quiet beauty and now I'm 81.
Was I going to die there too,
stacking wood, chopping kindling,
wildfire danger, fierce tree-twisting winds,
problems with the water system,
and checking my shoes for scorpions?

So now I'm in town—
a secluded skylit cottage
I can vacuum in ten minutes.
Sweet garden too, with
towering purple potato vine, six tiny tomato plants.
Two blocks from friends,
less than a mile from my daughter
who can walk here with her crutches
along the river path.
My landlady gives me the newspaper
I give her *The New Yorker.*

SANTA CRUZ MONDAY
DENA TAYLOR

Not trusting my legs
on our morning hike
I turn back at the rickety steps
say I'll see everyone later
at the picnic tables
where I read *The New Yorker*
watch surfers scramble barefoot
over wet and rounded rocks.

Later I visit Barbara in the acute care center
where she says she doesn't need anything
but looks miserable
face scrunched, eyes closed.
Tell Phyllis I love her, she says
She'll know what I mean.

Now I watch a hummingbird
and white butterfly
flit around the marigolds.
Should go in, send emails, return calls
work on my book—
first some ice cream
with blueberries.

SORTING PHOTOGRAPHS
CONSTANCE CRAWFORD

I'll keep this picture, it shows a truth about me
that I want them to see, my children
and whoever else is interested.
I have not left my mark the way I'd hoped—
except of course on my successive houses,
my handsome, well-run houses.
But who knows who I am
and what I've been through? No one.
I was close to sixty here, after the children were gone
and I had time to read and think; dressed well;
my husband came in and saw me there
in the living room chair reading a book.
He had one of his precious cameras
with him. He aimed it at me and snapped the shutter—
even after everything we'd said that morning.
I remember it well. He knew I detest
having my picture taken.
This time I looked straight at the lens
and let it be myself it saw and recorded.
I should probably destroy this picture,
the hatred that pours out of it.

But, in a way, I like my looks, my skirt fits well
and one blue and white spectator pump is off,
lying on its side. I like that touch.
I'm going to keep this picture
and let my eldest daughter find it,
loose in the box with no explanation
just to the knee. My good legs are crossed.

A Widow Reads Robinson Crusoe
Jean Nordhaus

Islanded, he must have been surprised
as she to find herself alone
in a season when even the winged
seeds of the maple come paired.

She admires his ingenuity
and how, bereft, he never lacks for comfort—
how from the wreckage of hope, he built
a habitation and fortified it
with a palisade of still-green sticks
that rooted in a self-renewing wall.

Slowly, taking pains, he taught himself
to fire cooking pots of clay, grind flour
for bread. Inventing agriculture,
rediscovering animal husbandry
and tailoring, he built a life
not so unlike the life he'd left. Once

from a felled tree, he carved a boat
so big he couldn't drag it to the water.
He started over, dug a smaller
vessel he could launch—for time
was what he had—twenty-eight
years, long enough to marry
and to raise a child....

It's night. The telephone lies still.
Beside her looms the empty bed
unmapped and dangerous
as sleep. And so she pulls the afghan close
settles her glasses on her nose and reads.

Lost Words
Jean Nordhaus

I walked to the corner
to mail my letter to the world

but the mailbox was gone

nothing where it stood so long
except an absence
and the rusty bus-stop sign—

not even a residual
flange or bolt
to break the mute rhythm
of herringbone brick.

Iron of generations,
iron of over 50 years of waiting—
gone

along with all the thanks,
apologies, checks, invitations,
poems and petitions

I delivered over decades
to its wide blue mouth

watching the stamped envelopes
slide beyond my grasp and recall
into the black vortex

much like the words
I keep losing these days:

lilac,
      ramparts,
            brassica,

That flower with the
jester's cap and bells—

as one by one they slip
into the mind's abyss

Tylenol,
      lantana
           columbine

beyond all grasp and recall

WIDOW AT COCKTAIL PARTY
LUCILLE GANG SHULKLAPPER

To make a dramatic entrance, wearing a new wig, and an old black dress,
hoping no one will see you trip on the door ledge, your bleeding toe.

To stand on the side, searching for a familiar face, strange faces posed
in slouched ease, caked makeup, disinterested, yet interested in the

passing trays of battered shrimp, deep fried, little pink tails upright
for dipping in fiery sauce, or holding the shell of themselves.

To catch the eye of a black-tied waiter with a tray of perspiring glasses,
to leave the empty ones untouched, hold the full glass. To raise the rim,

spilling the wine as you sip, like the coffee you pour from its decanter
wanting to cling to it, grinding itself into bits, staining flossed teeth.

To make conversation with walls of white-washed paint, halls of fun houses
built on stilts to escape leaking dams, broken levees. To sit

on the lingering chair near the door; to feel its fragile feet tipping
its plumped body, deodorized dust mites, on the patterned carpet.

To look for the women's room, once the lady's room, now the rest room
down the hallway where self-flushing toilets work and hot air dryers blow.

To return to the ballroom, to hear drum rolls of music announce dinner.
Soup or salad? Fish or chicken? Fruit or ice cream? To remember

what you wanted, or did not want, to pick up or put down the fork,
to wonder if the knife is sharp enough to slit your wrists.

A New Cord
Gunilla Norris

around my neck
carries the chunky weight
of the GPS that now hangs
flat against my heart.
I'm banded at eighty.

Someone will always know
where I am, even if I don't, or
even if I don't want to know.
I lie down under a tree,
on the sweet breathing ground,

beneath a full canopy of rustling
green, and I sense the lost joy
of being invisible. I gaze up,
a lifetime's habit, and then
I remember how to climb through

the maze of branches, up, up to
the treetop that's bowing with
my soul's weight as we meet, old
friends. Even so, I'll be found.
Someone will know where I am,

Gone is the joy of being elsewhere
without a trace. But something in me
wants to believe that even tracked
I'll be free. They might think
they'll find me, but they won't.

Etta's Bentwood Rocking Chair
Deena Linett

She's sitting in the old bentwood rocker
given her by his mother. Which is how
she thinks of it, though in fact it came
to her after Anton, her first husband, died.

His mother had been kind and dear
and he was harsh and sometimes mean.
He seemed to think she was there
to serve him. One day, she thought

    I am not, and she left.

Fifty-eight years went by—we don't know
where they go or what has happened in them
but her four children—he did give her those—
were beautiful and healthy. They grew up

and into middle age, and one day the second son
stopped by. Our father's ill, he told her,
and I think he's dying. He phoned his brother
and sisters and they had a meeting.

They didn't tell her and she didn't ask.

When he died they wanted to give her the chair,
making a fuss about it to announce the arrival.

For a long time she couldn't speak.
But then she remembered to say Thank You.

She thought about it for many days,
and the seasons changed. The rocker
was supposed to be comforting but it was not.

Or it didn't suit, here. She didn't want him back,
nor the chair, but she couldn't drag it to the street
for the trash now that she was over eighty;
she might trip. And besides, it was a gift

from her good mother-in-law. Well, no.
From the children. She thought to put it
where the wind blew rain against the window
    —she could leave it open—and then

she began to put used newspapers on it,
or grocery bags, emptied and folded.
She never swore, but if she had, she would've said
    I do not want that damned chair,

though sometimes she missed her mother-in-law.

One day she pulled it to the space near the door
to the yard with the shovels and boots and rain gear.
A few weeks later she dragged it out
onto the little porch outside the back door

and she was pleased: it rather belonged there,
she thought. And then one day
there was a lot more light coming in
from the windows in that door

and she looked out. The cherry tree
was blooming, and the wind
tossing branches like a God-given fan
and she saw that someone had taken it.

At long last! she exclaimed, and cried.
And the tree made cherries, and the wind
scraped branches against the house
and there was a lovely light

outside the back door and down the steps
to the spring-green yard, where cherries
had blown here and there
and she thought of *manna*, and was glad.

AFTERLIFE
KATHERINE WILLIAMS

After I didn't call 911 because I didn't want to wake the neighbors,
after I went back to sleep and didn't die, here is this morning,
fresher than yesterday because I might not have seen it at all.
In the street, such amplitude – an absence of movement or sound.
A single crisp leaf lies on the air, though I feel no wind.

This quiet is like the house when my husband would travel,
each object more vivid, backlit by his sure return.
No one much returns these days—lifting off as they do to other realms.
Some nights I try to find a place in the street under a smudge of sky
where the trees don't block the stars, but even then
the light from the streetlight blankets the view.

Knowing the stars are up there should be enough.
                    Memory should be enough.
But I'm thirsty for the actual light of stars
                    still shining eons after their end.

APOLOGIES AT A CERTAIN AGE
NANCY SMILER LEVINSON

I apologize for opening a suspicious email
I apologize that my password list is not updated
I apologize for my erroneous bank sign-in and getting locked out
That I forgot to order new checks on time
Losing the safety deposit box key
I apologize that I tried unjamming my printer before making a call
I apologize that I reached for the crystal vase without using a step stool
For dropping an oven mitt on the hot stove top
For leaving the oven on overnight
I know I misplaced my credit card, and for that I apologize

I apologize for not muting myself during a live music program
For not realizing that I was unmuted
For answering the phone and talking
For my unconscionable disruption
I apologize for the slip of my potty mouth

I apologize for crying to my grown children
For crying
But I found my credit card

BLAME IT ON DOROTHY
HERMIE MEDLEY

My mother was strong on manners. I remember her
words, "Always be polite to others, and that includes how
you talk on the telephone." In 1925, when I was five, we
purchased our first phone, which was fastened over my
head on the living room wall. I had to climb up on a
chair, dial the operator, and ask her to "Connect me to
my Grandma Palmer at 247-J, please." I used equally
good manners with my aunts and grandparents as with
the operator. Those were the years I listened to what my
parents told me and believed every word. "Bring up a
child in the way he should go, and when he is old, he
will not depart from it," was a Bible verse thoroughly
espoused by my parents. As time went by, I departed
from the ways they thought God had in mind for me,
though when it came to telephone manners, I was a
stickler. Until lately anyway. Until Dorothy started ringing
me up at dinnertime to offer me a mortgage on the
home I do not own, do not ever want to own, either now
or in any life to follow. I heard her out night after night
with great courtesy. Until last Thursday. That night the
devil must have had me in his power, because the
moment I heard her cheery voice, just as I'd started to
eat, I slammed the phone down, slammed it hard. I've
done the same thing every night since. Ahhh—what a
freeing experience, what a release, what joy!

DEAD OF NIGHT
KIRSTEN MORGAN

My return to consciousness is instantaneous. A deep dream, the wandering kind, is suddenly punctuated with a sharp electronic sound—the exact noise our alarm system makes when a door is opened. Since it's 2:30 a.m., I zoom from a parallel universe to eye-popping alertness in a few seconds. Someone has entered our house.

Clicking off possibilities yields the memory that my daughter had dropped by that afternoon and had quite possibly exited through the front door without remembering to turn the lock. Or, the sound could have been part of my dream. Am I willing to take a chance on the latter? Not on my life.

Within seconds, I run through a gamut of response protocols, but the one that speaks most loudly is to put my vulnerable body behind a locked door as quickly as possible. I snatch up several pillows from the bed, throw them into the bathtub of the adjoining bathroom, grab my warm robe and lock myself in. When the shaking abates and my breath slows a bit, I reassess the situation. If this is someone bent on murder, I'm toast. If he wants mayhem, I'm helpless. But, if he intends to snoop and help himself to my purse, phone, and nonexistent jewelry, I will lie very quietly in my puffy tub and let him have at it, hoping he won't have an insatiable desire for some bath soap and toothpaste as well.

My feet are fish on ice, my heart still jounces and it's only 2:40. Sleep will be impossible, so I entertain myself by conjuring newspaper headlines: *Elderly Woman Snuffed Out in Pillowed Bathtub* or *Quiet Suburb Shocked,* or, my favorite, *Husband Snores While Wife Battles Ax Murderer.* Exhausting this unusual but interesting exercise, I try to settle into some level of quasi-comfort by attempting meditation, or at least deep breathing, but it turns into raspy, panting half breaths. The house entertains me by presenting its symphony of night sounds—cracking pipes, settling walls, popping icemaker, a bit of wind against the tree that in turn groans against the gutter. And, of course, the sound of footsteps. Lots of footsteps, even though our house is spread with thick carpet over concrete.

After three hours, or maybe thirty minutes, I become wildly hungry, to say nothing of cold, stiff, and not a little angry with this creep who has invited himself into our house, interrupted my sleep, sent me to the bathtub and scared the wits out of me just because he feels like it. I can see him slithering through my private space—long, greasy hair, stoned, unimpressed with my decorating skills, disdainful of my objets d'art, and I become both more enraged and more resolved to challenge him to make my day—or night.

I look around for a weapon. Other than a dainty, pink plastic razor with a dull blade, there's only one option: *Elderly Woman Clobbers Burglar with Bath Oil Bottle.* My daughter had given it to me for my birthday—expensive bubbly stuff in a clear, cabernet bottle. I am loath to waste it on the head of an intruder, but balance parsimony against survival and decide it's worth the loss and mess. After testing its heft and weight, I push the cork in tighter so the contents won't spray all over the rug, practice swinging it around and plan my strategy. I'll silently unlock the bathroom door, open the bedroom door and peek through to see whether lights have been turned on, or perhaps note a flashlight beam playing around the living room. If the intruder is outside the door, he won't be expecting a bath oil bash, so I can deliver it and then run like hell. If he isn't waiting, but something seems awry, I'll slip out the door conveniently located in the adjoining bedroom and dash— over snow, through freezing temps, toward any neighbor who might open the door in the middle of the night. By my reckoning, that would be none, but it's my only chance. *Bag of Bones Found Frozen in a Snowbank; Thought to be Woman Missing Since March.*

It's an ingenious scheme and the more I think about it, the more committed I become to taking charge of this situation. I won't be held hostage in my own bathroom, and certainly not without a snack. Regardless of grammar, it's him or me, now or never. I turn the doorknob to peek down the darkened hallway, but there's only one problem with the execution of my perfect plan: instead of opening quietly, the door creaks like a horror movie, loudly announcing my presence. Although a sane person would have sprinted back into the bathroom or out the back door, I suddenly feel strongly that my house is empty of intruders and that I can, with steady nerves and a jolt of brio, reclaim it. This assumption is based on absolutely nothing, but it feels empowering and I don't seem able to stop myself. I creep like a gray panther in a pink bathrobe down the hall toward the kitchen and living room, bath oil in my raised hand. I decide to leave the hall light off, not wanting to show up in that spotlight, even though I have the advantage of a semi-deadly weapon. *Old Gal Has Gumption, Lacks Judgment.*

Five steps, ten. Stop and listen. Fifteen—silence. Only five more and I'm in the entry, sensing no motion or heavy breathing (other than my own) either in the kitchen to my right or in the living room, straight ahead. This will be the final test. My heart now clattering like dropped dishes, I creep to the front door and turn the knob. It's locked. The door is locked! The only portal an intruder could have easily entered is secured. Even the deadbolt is on. *Golden Oldie Expires Next to Locked Door; Investigators Baffled.*

I turn on lights, quickly check the garden room door—locked. Just to be sure, I try the handle on the door to the garage. Tight and safe. If I'd been a normal person, I would have collapsed on the couch with a bottle of gin and a box of chocolates, but instead I pour a bowl of grape nuts, brew some Sleepytime tea, and ponder the events of this bizarre nighttime non-caper. And I'm dumbfounded as I slowly come to understand the absolute inanity, the astonishing audacity, the stunning temerity I had somehow gathered in order to walk toward a potential burglar in the middle of the night, armed with bath oil, believing I had the advantage, or at least thinking we were an equal match. *Lonely Granny Contrives 'Ordeal,' Hoping to be Noticed.*

SPEED LINES
MARILYN ROBERTSON

I can feel those comic book speed lines today,
streaking off my elbows and heels

as I leave the recent past
in a blustery cloud of old news.

You can talk about time standing still
but when has it ever done that?

All of us racing along at 900 miles an hour,
hurtling toward whatever lies ahead,

while at the same time, everything
in this room—armchair, lamp, piano—

stays right where it's always been,
reliable as ever.

Everything moves.
And nothing does.

I think that's enough paradox for one day.

THIS IS THE TIME
SYLVIA BORTIN PATIENCE

The wind whines around
corners of the house, its sound
brings rain, brings Spring,

though in the quiet within
the fire and hearth are still
the center of my home.

Early awake I wait
in whispering darkness
for the morning light to come.

This is the time beyond
the monthly bleeding
cycles of fertility, ability

to bear another child.
This is the time of weekly
phone calls, long distance,

of souvenirs and memories:
this photograph, that shell,
a silver ring;
the time of learning how
to live alone, to take
long walks along the beach,
and solo hikes,

to know again, become
best friends with my own aging
face within the mirror.

HONEYED DAYS
SYLVIA BYRNE POLLACK

I used to believe old age was absurd,
expected to live hard and die early.
How astounding I'm writing these words.

You know that proverb about early birds?
I guess worms are OK if you're hungry.
I used to believe old age was absurd,

sedate minuet on a harpsichord
but even minuets can swing jively.
How astounding I'm humming these words,

not laid out in a box made of pine boards,
or just fragments—the rest up the chimney.
I used to believe old age was absurd,

now enjoy honeyed days unfettered.
To some I'm the object of envy!
How astounding I'm thinking these words.

It turns out that life is a smorgasbord—
mortality, frugality, chutney.
I used to believe old age was absurd.
How astounding I'm singing these words.

TREASURED MOMENTS
JEANIE GREENSFELDER

Age twelve, I stood on a bus,
saw a woman with white hair
and thought, *You have always
been old. I will always be young.*

Magical thinking failed.

My turn came to be a period piece,
often unseen, yet alive with new
perspectives and heartfelt pleasures.

Mary Oliver said, "Tell me,
what is it you plan to do with your
one wild and precious life?"

Now, I say, *What is it you plan to do
with this one wild and precious day?*

This morning on my beach stroll
a woman my age needing two walking sticks
reached Morro Rock. We smiled. She saw
that I saw, and I saw that she saw

how we treasured moments.

THIS HAPPINESS
CAROLE STONE

To be in the kitchen,
darkness coming on,
backyard hill fading
into the landscape,
deer no longer
climbing down,
these apparitions of nature,
haunting the suburbs.

On WQXR, Haydn,
and me dancing little steps,
thinking lucky, O lucky,
as I count my years
on my fingers.

I haven't left my house
for days, waiting for the sun
like a refilled prescription.
Who said, "Old age
ain't for sissies?"

My brother, Jerry,
an aficionado
of Forties movies
said it was Bette Davis.

And yet, this happiness
in my kitchen, slicing
an acorn squash,
squeezing lemon
on the flounder.
Just me.

Part Two

THE WIDE WORLD

All new learning looks at first like chaos.
Change is not a threat to your life but an invitation to live.
—Adrienne Rich, 1929-2012
American poet, essayist, and feminist writer.

Living is a form of not being sure, not knowing what next or how....
We guess. We may be wrong, but we take leap after leap in the dark.
—Agnes DeMille, 1905-1993
American dancer and choreographer.

I am always looking for new ways to learn and grow, and I believe that
there is no limit to what a person can achieve if they have the courage to
pursue their dreams.
—Caroline Herschel, 1750-1848
German-British scientist, considered to be
the first professional female astronomer.

I was excited at something new, always liked something new, but give
credit to everybody who helped. I didn't do anything alone but try to go
to the root of the question and succeeded there.
—Katherine Johnson, 1918-2020
American mathematician
whose calculations on flight paths for spacecrafts
were critical to NASA space flights.

HUBRIS
KIRSTEN MORGAN

Let's face it. No one looks forward to turning 80, that in-your-face har-
binger of doom. We can congratulate ourselves on still feeling pretty
good; for outliving half of our peers; on often being mistaken for a mere
75, but none of that mitigates the onus of the age. Each of the other
decade arrivals seemed interesting—an accomplishment rather than
assumption of diminishment, but eight and zero in combination present an unmatched gravitas. It's the big turning point from flirting with
old age to actually arriving there. It's the frustration of watching others
tuck you into their expectations satchel.

So, to prove them wrong, my brain begins to busy itself with creating
alternative scenarios instead of settling into the rocker with an afghan
on my lap. Denial. A desperate response to the inevitable.

I feel fine. Oh yeah, my stamina is attenuated, my right thumb joint
has a bit of arthritis, my back seizes up now and then, and my face
carries a net of fine wrinkles with a few deeper etchings here and there,
but I believe myself reasonably fit and moderately strong. I realize the
rate of change is greater with each passing year, so I harbor no delusions
about winning any races with Father Time, but my issue is with now,
this very day, this year, this period of my life when I remain relatively
unchanged but have nonetheless been categorized by others as some-
what unhinged. I can't do anything about it but accept this scarlet A as
a mark of pride—which I'm learning to do—but still. But still.

I decide to engage in a series of small challenges, to steer my psyche
toward what to retain and what to relinquish with as much grace as I
can muster. So, on September 3rd, with the realization that winter is
about to move in, both meteorologically and physiologically, I decide
to venture from my Denver home to the top of the Rockies, the Con-
tinental Divide Trail on the east side of the summit of Berthoud Pass,
with a starting elevation of 11,300 feet. This is a hike I've done many
times over the years, but it now occurs to me that, as a person of 80,
any of these hikes could be my last. It's definitely harder now to travel
miles at elevation than it was even a few years ago, so I decide to do a

small hike and turn around when energy begins to drain away—perhaps a couple of miles. I bring about 10 ounces of water, enough for a couple of miles, and a windbreaker to wear over my light down jacket on this sunny day. All is well.

I start late, 7:00 a.m. The trail is almost deserted, the temperature in the comfy forties and the sky relatively cloudless. After a couple of miles, the trail becomes less steep, so I continue, disrupted only by 40 or so high school girls on a fall outing who barrel past me with ease, probably wondering why some old broad is huffing along their trail. I feel good, so I just keep hiking—at the top of the world, with views in all directions, including down toward the snaking highway to the west and a collection of elegant tarns (tiny mountain lakes) tucked into green slopes on the east. I stop a couple of times to let people pass or take in the view, but I mostly just keep a slow and steady pace, with no destination or time in mind.

I begin to wonder how close I could come to a long wished-for destination, Mt. Flora, 13,170 ft. above sea level. I decide to keep going. By now a couple of hours have passed. The elevation, according to my phone, is well over 12,000 feet. The mountain air feels welcoming. Drifting clouds join in the joy of this day. So I continue, stopping now and then, passing the last of familiar terrain and heading up at a more steady climb. I drink a little water but decide to protect my small supply on the small chance that I can keep going longer.

A few other hardy souls pass me, most with dogs, as though it were dog day and I was the odd one to be hiking sans canine companion. All other hikers are, of course, at least 50 years younger than I, which seems like such a strange thing to say, especially since I was 30 not long ago.

My energy is fading considerably, but I see the Mt. Flora peak and start to wonder whether I could possibly have enough tucked away to get even closer. By now I'm at nearly 13,000 feet and stopping after each hundred steps. Then I'm stopping and sitting on a rock for a few minutes. An occasional sip of water is all I can afford. I ponder asking a passing hiker for an extra ounce, but pride disallows this concession. Mountain tops are always very rocky, so, although there's a path, the footing is consistently uneven, with loose rocks from baseball to football size as part of the walkway, punctuated with the occasional boulder field. It seems as if almost every rock is also tilted at an angle that precludes solid footing. Thank goodness I remembered to bring hiking poles this time. By now I'm above 12,500. I occasionally take my pulse, which has stayed at around 100 bpm but returns to 80 or so with a few minutes of rest. People are still passing me at a brisk pace; at least someone will be around to administer CPR.

It takes another hour or so to make the final ascent, but I push through with everything I have and suddenly there it is, with a crooked wooden sign announcing that I am on top of Mt. Flora, with an elevation of 13,170 ft. An 80-year-old body that has consumed seven ounces of water in over three hours has just gained 1800 feet of elevation and lived to tell the tale. What on earth was I thinking when I set out? I've hiked all my life and am always relentlessly prepared. This was meant to be a stroll—two hours at most. But after all, I'm 80, so am undoubtedly losing my way through a thickening brain maze.

Going down will be a snap, I tell myself after taking a selfie with the Mt. Flora sign in the background and sending a braggy text to my kids. Then I look west instead of north. It's only 11:00, but the clouds are beginning to gather into what could be an afternoon storm, the one that only seems to happen when hikers are far from the car. Because of those pesky loose rocks, this will be even slower going than the ascent. Extremely proud of this notch in my aging belt, I chug a few more ounces of now-precious water and make my way carefully down the pitch, legs even more wobbly than on the ascent.

Another half hour and I begin to wonder about the wisdom of every decision I had made. The entire western sky is blackening and rumbling, moving slowly toward me but still at a distance. I pick up my pace. Two miles from the car and still 12,000 feet closer to sky, it begins to rain a bit. I'm alert but only moderately concerned. Within minutes, the rain turns to bb-size hail, the wind picks up, and the temperature plummets. I walk faster, but still have to be careful of loose rocks. It isn't steep at this point but is far from flat. And then it really starts to rain—and I start to run at a slow pace, my down sweater soaked and windbreaker providing absolutely no protection.

I, who haven't run for 15 years, now realize that this pace could be deadly, so I pick up speed with at least a mile still ahead—in pouring rain, with great thunder crashes all around and the wind still whipping. Soon I'm bolting down the access road, but rather than feeling safer, I feel vulnerable to lightning out in the open. It's even more dangerous to seek shelter beneath a tree. During those endless 20 minutes, I streak like a madwoman in great strides, gasping for breath, the muscles in my legs on fire. I'm afraid they'll just give out, along with my pounding heart, but somehow my entire body joins forces to make the impossible happen. Leaping over rivulets now carved in the dirt road, I thank Zeus every time a thunder boom means its accompanying streak of lightning hasn't noticed me.

I keep imagining someone finding my charred remains just feet from the car and convince myself that departing in a flash of glory might be interesting. But maybe another time. Now I just want to survive these final few hundred yards. I see the car, spring through what feels like waist-deep water instead of small, crazed streams sluicing the road.

I'm there. I jerk open the door and leap in. For some reason, I lock the door. Panting, laughing and crying, I start the car and turn the heater to blast furnace and the seat warmer to grill level.

The rain is bucketing, thunder and lightning chase each other and me as I drive down the pass with greatest care, but none of this matters.

I am 80 and I've mastered the mountain. I've conquered the storm. I'm freezing, my teeth are clattering like typewriter keys, my hands are blue as they try to grip the steering wheel and my entire body is covered with an icy film of frozen rain. But I've arrived in this decade with panache and brio. Surely everything else will be a snap—as long as I bring enough water and start early.

LAST DAY AT FATTAH'S HOUSE
DENA TAYLOR

Lahcen drove us to the hammam
in a town south of Marrakesh.
The scene there so different
from the women we'd seen in the streets,
many with hijabs, a handful with black niqabs,
the hair and body coverings.
Here, no one wore more than underpants
some not even that.
The women were smiling, talking, relaxed
scrubbing themselves and their children
completely comfortable with their bodies.
A sense of community, warmth, so palpable --
time stopped in this bathhouse
where they washed us clean.

Later that day, several men,
relatives and friends of Fattah,
musicians, came to the house.
They played and sang for hours
with instruments I'd never seen.
So full of joy, their friendship so evident.
Smiles, laughter, love in their eyes
appreciating each other.

These men, those women—
we saw the humanity of Morocco in them.

THE NEW COMPUTER
JANICE ALPER

When I married my husband, Marv, in 1962, he worked for IBM. "There will be a computer in every home in twenty-five years."

Adoringly, I looked up and him and laughed, "You're nuts."

Marv died almost ten years ago, and I was left with five computers. Since then, I downsized to one computer, one tablet, and one trusty cell phone. About five years ago I bought a state-of-the-art two-in-one HP laptop. I learned to use Windows 10, became adept at creating documents, archiving what I needed, and always found what I was looking for, even if it was years old. Everything was stored in its proper place.

Like me, the HP got tired. It still worked well but seemed to be slowing down a bit. Besides, it was heavy and lugging it around became burdensome, especially for my newly fused back. So, shopping for a new computer I went.

My Trusty Advisor (TA) said "Get a Dell. Don't let the guys at the store sell you anything else."

Off I went to my local blue and gold store and realized that what has happened to affordable housing seems to have happened to affordable computers for older ladies. I checked at the university bookstore, which was even higher. Trusty Amazon (different TA) to the rescue.

My shiny, lightweight, two-in-one Dell computer arrived. It took a few days for TA to come by to set it up. Within an hour he got things working, deftly transferred files via external disc to the new computer. He even set up my home page so that when I log on there is Marv smiling at me from a vineyard in Julian in a photograph taken six months before he died…great comfort.

TA advised, "This has Windows 11 on it. You'll have to learn how to use it, but I suspect it is not too difficult."

Left on my own I discovered Windows 11 is not so easy and I kept losing documents. My young neighbors, who are of the correct age, came by, and showed me all was not lost and figured it out. I wrote everything down, but I am still struggling.

On a zoom writing group, I noticed all my background pictures were gone. The neighbors came by again, showed me how to upload the photos, but when I tried it myself, I failed miserably. I'm still working on it.

And where are my seventeen thousand pictures? TA showed me how to get to them off the external drive, but he didn't explain how to upload them, or I may have missed that lesson.

I write all the instructions down in a handy little notebook, spend hours looking for something, go to the refrigerator, because that's what writers do when they are frustrated, sit down and play some computer games. After broadening my aging hips, and feeling relaxed, there are "Aha moments." I get on with my abandoned tasks and manage to complete something.

This has been a steep learning curve for me, but tenacity is my middle name, and I will just keep plodding along. I'm sure one day I'll get it right, but by then it will be time for a new computer.

GIVE A LITTLE WHISTLE
MARILYN REYNOLDS

When I open the front door for my friend to leave, my miniature poodle, Lily, zips out to the sidewalk where she then sits facing me. I don't know if she's truly a miniature poodle. She has a checkered past and is of unknown descent. The one thing I have managed to teach her is to come when called. After a myriad of practices with high-value treats, she unfailingly comes running to me, top speed, from wherever, whenever I call her. Unfailingly, that is, until today. Today she sits unmoving on the sidewalk, looking at me.

"Lily, come!" I call again.

She sits still as a statue, watching.

"LILY, COME!" I repeat and repeat. She sits and sits.

My friend Anara, standing on the front porch witnessing the rebellion, purses her lips and whistles. Lily comes running! She stops before me and sits in the "I-expect-my-treat-now" position. I don't think so, Lily.

Later in the day I decide to experiment. Lily is at her usual post in front of the kitchen slider, looking out on the patio. I'm in my office. I lick my lips, purse, and blow. There is only the slightest sound of exhaled breath. I try again. Nothing. What??? I've been able to whistle since I was four years old and now I can't whistle? Is whistling one of those skills old people lose, like turning cartwheels and remembering phone numbers?

I never did learn that two-fingered, ear-piercing whistle that the across-the-street neighbor used to call her kids in at dinnertime, but I could whistle to get someone's attention. I could whistle a tune! I try to think back to the last time I whistled. Nothing comes to mind. I again purse my lips and blow. Still no sound.

Except for Anara, I also can't remember the last time I even heard someone whistle. It gets me wondering if the practice of whistling has fallen by the wayside, like burning trash, or taking pictures with a camera. It seemed everyone whistled when I was growing up in that little town of Temple City in Southern California. My father whistled a low tune while he sliced lunchmeat, or ground hamburger, or swept the sawdust in his meat market. My cousin Jim whistled on his morning walk to work in that same market. I don't think I ever heard my granny whistle. Maybe she couldn't whistle with false teeth.

In the privacy of my car, I experiment with blowing air through various mouth/tongue positions. I'm determined to get my whistle back but so far, no luck. At home I look to YouTube for whistling help. You can learn anything on YouTube. Just last week YouTube taught me how to unplug my toilet without using a plunger; surely it can help me regain my whistle.

I've made my peace with never again doing a cartwheel, or standing on my head, or even getting up from the floor without first awkwardly turning to a hands and knees crawling position and bumbling myself upward. But I'm not willing to never whistle again, goddamn it!

Sure enough, several possibilities come up on YouTube—tutorials on how to whistle loudly, with fingers, without fingers, etc. I choose "How to whistle in 3 EASY Steps!" First there's an ad for "Mandalorian," reminding me that Disney has moved far beyond Bambi. Then there's loud, grating music, not whistling, accompanying the name of the whistle teacher in large, three-dimensional letters. Let's call him LARRY O for the sake of anonymity. He starts out with "What's up guys?" which reminds me that this is not a video directed at my demographic. Then he proceeds to talk so fast I can barely understand him. Then, while he's telling us that several people, some of them actual friends, have been begging him to make such a video, a message flashes on the screen saying, "Let's try to reach 40 likes guys!"

I'm already so irritated by LARRY O's talking at top speed and addressing me as a guy, I'm ready to switch to the "Whistling Tutorial (without fingers)." But as annoying as this "guy" is, he at least knows how to use an apostrophe, so I'll give him another minute. LARRY O's first tip is to say the word "two" and leave your lips in that position, the right spot for whistling. I do that. Next, position your tongue against your bottom teeth. "Yike iss," he says, trying to demonstrate the position and talk at the same time. Then he says to cave your tongue in the middle and leave the sides higher. My tongue won't cave in the middle, so I skip to the last step—blow lightly. Yes!! There's a sound! Probably not enough to call Lily with, but a step in the right direction!

I decide LARRY O's not so bad after all. His fast-talking, nervous hair-touching gestures, the pimple on his forehead, and his video's bland beige background in what is probably his childhood bedroom, all elicit a sort of motherly empathy—or more age appropriately, great-grandmotherly empathy. I make another whistle sound, this time with two tones. Faint, but still . . . I'm so happy that I leave a thumbs up. I don't, though, succumb to Larry's pitch to subscribe to his videos. He's already taught me what I need to know.

In the week that follows, I practice whistling when I'm alone in the car, or when Lily's not around. I want to wait until my whistle is strong before she hears it, but I've now got a pretty good "Jingle Bells."

In addition to practicing my whistle, the subject of whistling keeps pushing up through my subconscious to demand attention. The phrase "clean as a whistle" jumps to mind as I wipe down the kitchen counter. The seven dwarfs march across my consciousness singing and whistling their familiar rendition of "Whistle While You Work." I'm thinking about a whistleblower in the news recently who exposed the horrendous conditions children were living in at ICE facilities at the U.S.-Mexico border. And then the old scary radio program, "The Whistler," comes to mind. I turn to Ms. Google, who plays the opening tune from a 1946 broadcast. There is the creaking door, the spooky whistled tune that ends with a harsh minor chord, the voice of the mysterious Whistler who knows "the many secrets hidden in the hearts of men and women" and "the nameless terrors of which they dare not speak."

I mustn't let the past outweigh the present, so I leave "The Whistler" and turn to that place we're all advised to live, "in the now." I water the parched patio plants. I read new email. Later, while Lily is outside, napping in her favorite patio chair, I stand just inside the door, lick my lips, purse them in the "two" position, and blow out an acceptably strong whistle. Lily rouses! She runs through the dog door and sits at my feet in treat position! I shower her with treats and praise. Several times over the course of the day I whistle for her. Several times she comes. I'm as pleased with myself over this revived skill as I was a few weeks ago when I finished my 1,000-piece jigsaw puzzle depicting Nancy Drew book covers. Maybe the key to happiness at 85 is meeting a simple, self-set challenge. I'm not sure what's next—maybe perfecting the finger snap.

Or maybe honing my whistling skill to reproduce "The Whistler's" theme song. It won't be cartwheels.

PAUL HAD IT RIGHT ON THE BUTTON
HERMIE MEDLEY

The night after I signed up for a writing group on spirituality, I was unable to fall asleep. Whatever had given me the notion I knew anything about the subject anyway? I couldn't even tell you what spirituality is, let alone write a poem about it. I crawled out of bed and pulled the dictionary off the shelf. Head propped on two pillows, I looked up "spirituality" in my decrepit old Webster's.

"The state of being spiritual," it informed me.

"Oh, thanks a lot," I replied. Then I looked under some related words until I found where it said that spirit is the part of the human being associated with mind and feeling, as distinguished from the physical body. That sounded pretty good to me. It made me think of my father, who always watched his thoughts and behavior. When any member of his family got negative, he'd quote from one of his favorite parts of the Bible,

"Whatsoever things are honorable, whatsoever is just, whatsoever is pure, whatsoever is lovely, whatsoever is gracious, if there is anything worthy of praise, think about those things."

Even though St. Paul was a male chauvinist pig in my uncharitable opinion, I realized his spiritual advice is what I've tried to practice most of my life. I dropped the dictionary on the floor and fell asleep in less than five minutes.

Art Nouveaux Necklace by Fereshteh Fatemi

BEYOND ME
JUDY DAVIDSON

"The names of the colors are sometimes cages containing what doesn't belong there, and this is often true of language generally, the words like women, men, child, adult, safe, strong, three, true, black, white, rich, poor. We need the words, but use them best knowing they are containers forever spilling over and breaking open. Something is always beyond."
— Rebecca Solnit, *Reflections of My Nonexistence.*

The words that captured my attention: "*something is always beyond,*" "*cages,*" "*my nonexistence.*"

I just watched a program that described the recent launch of the new satellite, the James Webb Space Telescope, which is designed to replace and outpace the aging Hubble Telescope. If successful, we will be able to see new worlds that we might have only previously imagined, millions of miles away. I have some hiking companions who ramble on about "dark matter." Their scientific language is a mystery of its own just as *what is actually out there* has been until now.

Welcome to a new world, I think to myself... a world beyond our greatest imaginings as prisoners of a limited earth. I am struck by the sense of implied infinity—the universe or multiple universes that go on and on and on. I feel the contrast with our own sense of human limitation. We are born, we age (if we are lucky) and we die—never to return in our old form. Whether we come back as an imitation (or reincarnation) of ourselves, nobody really knows for sure. Despite religious teachings of being reborn *if we have been good enough,* there has never been definitive proof.

The words in Solnit's title, *Reflections of My Nonexistence,* hooked me. At the age of 79, I clearly have to face that my time on this mortal coil and my life as I have come to know it, will end. Maybe with a whimper, maybe with a big bang, who knows!

I have been spending the last month or so digging through many of the archives of my life—old paper files—the documents of a lifetime. Many of these items are pointless to save: manuals for old computers no longer in use, printouts of every exercise ever recommended by previous physical therapists for knee injuries, stiff neck and tender shoulders, *and* an endless supply of "articles of interest" clipped from magazines and newspapers. This is only a beginning summary of the effluvia. It is mostly normal stuff but definitely not essential to keep. Do I really need to keep all this stuff to validate my existence? Couldn't I just "be" before I come to my day "*not* to be"?

I ask myself, "What will remain of me when I am gone?" I will exist in the memory of others but for a limited period of time. People I have loved, befriended, worked with, and possibly helped, may look back and regret my passing and hold some treasured memories of our times together. But, alas, these people will also die. Who will I (and they) be then? Maybe dark matter, maybe a billion miles away in another world or God forbid, *nothing at all?*

When people talk about God creating man, I always get stuck with the puzzle "and who or what created God? How did it all get started?" I scratch my head in puzzlement. I am not unlike the space scientists who are pursuing the answers or non-answers to these deep questions about the origin of the universe or universes.

In my *p*ersistent *p*awing through my *p*rized *p*ossessions (enough already with all these P's!), I found a poem I had written to Stan on the 19th anniversary of our lives together or at least that is what the title said. It was a loving tribute to him and to the positive relationship we had managed to create despite earlier struggles.

So, what gets left is the fact that we have loved and we have been loved and nothing else really matters. Especially not the belongings, the trappings, or the glut of our possessions. Instead of constant battles for power, status, and wealth which will inevitably vanish, isn't it better to have left a legacy of love? I believe so, but it is a lesson that mankind fails to learn—over and over and over.

I recently have been focusing on my losses, allowing myself to drown in a muted state of sorrow. I could instead focus on what I have gained—a life that has had some merit, some value, even though ultimately it will be like a wisp in the eternal wind of time. If there truly is a beyond, maybe a piece of me will be there—rejoicing.

SPORTS BRA
JUDITH TERZI

First time a guy helps me buy a bra. Daniel
tells me bras hang from max to least support,
right to left. Like reading Arabic, I say. He

asks me my size for the heartiest armor—bras
with hooks. I hesitate. Like this gorgeous guy
cares what size an 80-year old wears? He says

bras *sans* hooks run small, medium, large,
calls me a medium. Turns out I'm a large. I take
three bras to try on—a humdrum black one

with hook & two blossomy ones without. Daniel
tucks me into a fitting room. What's the protocol
in these upscale sports boutiques? I tell him

not to check on me, just in case. Like Natasha
the week before at Macy's. Natasha took my
measurements. Natasha saw my naked breasts

while I tried on bras she brought me in a smaller
size. My husband saw them too; he was also there.
I try on the three bras—two with a labyrinth

of crisscross straps. I try stepping into these two
puzzles, jigsawing them over my hips or
maneuvering them over my head like a yogi.

These two bras never touch my breasts. The one
avec hook goes on like butter. I want to show
Daniel...but I remove it, put on my black 36D

Wacoal & sweatshirt to look for him. He's busy,
so Jason orders the full-support sports bra *avec*
hook. In lilac smoke. I look around—I'm the oldest

person here—triple or quadruple the age of anyone
else at Lululemon. BTW—they call salespeople
"educators" here. Not too old to learn a thing or two.

LAST STRAWS
MARILYN ROBERTSON

I renewed my driver's license the other day
and had to wait an extra-long time
because the fingerprint computer was down.

Whatever happened to ink? And the ritual
of the clerk rolling your thumb across the pad,
then across the paper so you could see those whorls
that set you apart from everyone else in the room.

This is the last straw, I said to the woman next to me.
Another bit of the old life tossed into the bin of oblivion
along with pay phones, typewriters, and mangles.

She said there was probably a truckload of last straws
headed our way. And for a moment I could see it:
the mowed field, a flash of pitchforks—

and the cows, coming home as they always have,
musing on the truth of idioms, the hunger of stomachs,
the vanishing of worlds.

THE PERILS
ADELE SHEDIAK

"I have Netflix"

The receptionist at the Medical Clinic
pauses
ponders my answer to her question
"What is your Supplemental Insurance?"

Friends, my Tribe, stew over password dilemmas
The Computer says
"Wrong"
We decide we all need an eight-year-old
for tech support

We thought we were doing "OK"
What will we be like at 90?

"Travel while you can" says Peg
as we sit in 1st Class on the train
to the top of Scotland
She's 90

We stop removing shoes and jackets
at 75
The screener at Charles de Gaulle replies
"Good for you"
When I inform her of my age
I then proceed to take off shoes and jacket
and submit to a pat-down
Apparently age doesn't matter in France

"I meant to say Health Net"

RESEARCH
MJ WERTHMAN WHITE

Mostly in obituaries, or occasionally
accompanying an interview,
I love the photos of elderly writers
captured in their preferred habitat,
the nonagenarians in wool cardigans
buttoned up against the winter-chill of age,
seamed faces harshly appraising the viewer
across the abyss of time;

invariably they are barricaded behind
a chaotic desk covered with squalls
of paper, with stacked Pisa-towers of books
poised to tumble at the slightest tremor.
The room's shelves are filled–crammed
with a lifetime's worth of reading.

I cut out pictures, adding each to my collection,
pasting them into journals, using a magnifying glass,
I read the book titles, seeking clues,
a way to be old like this.

THE FASTER, FASTER, FASTER CULTURE RANT
NAOMI NEWMAN

In this culture an old person shouldn't live so long. You're not wanted, respected, or appreciated. More like you're in the way. Get out of my way, Granny, I've got things to do, places to go, people to see, text messages to text message. I've got my I Phone, my I Pad, my I Pod, my I, I, I. You walk too slow, talk too slow, drive too slow, think too slow.

Things have got to happen sooner than now or it's too late. Too late to make a buck, or too late to win the game, or too late to get ahead. What needs satisfying *now* is all that matters. Not what my kids, or their kids, or their kids are going to have to pay for, or do without.

This is a culture where everything is obsolete by the time you open the unopenable package. And isn't this paranoid packaging an emblem of the insanity? Protect the gadget, not the environment. You've used the computer for a year—get the new model. It's better, it's sexier, it's what you've got to have, because if you don't, you won't be able to do everything faster, faster, faster than you're doing now. Also this new model will get you the love you want, the body you want, and eternal youth. Notice I say eternal youth, not life. Don't grow old, don't grow up, stay young—meaning undeveloped, immature, moody, needy, and perpetually unsatisfied while wholly dedicated to self-satisfaction.

Instead of mentors we have vendors. Instead of process we have products. We learn from manuals rather than from women and men. There's no place for the old, no avenue through which we can become respected Elders. There is no one who wants to hear what we've learned through living, and making mistakes and watching history unfold, because no one wants to stand still long enough to listen. How can we speak if there's no one to listen?

I Don't Want to Learn Anything New About Technology
Nancy Smiler Levinson

don't explain data base to me
don't teach me settings or apps
don't draw a diagram for me
don't walk me through
don't urge me to try the first step
don't tell me it's easy to put
three separate documents in one file

Do it for me

I don't have many years left
and attachments, WIFI and
differentiating id numbers
and admittance passwords
are not what I want or need to pursue
as I navigate skyward
in my endgame
Clouds are a mass of water drops
or ice crystals suspended in atmosphere
Cloud formations are infinite

Part Three

WHAT INSPIRES

Every woman who writes is a survivor.

—Tillie Olsen, 1912-2007
American feminist writer and activist.

When I found the beautiful white bones on the desert, I picked them up and took them home. I have used these things to say what is to me the wideness and wonder of the world as I live in it.

—Georgia O'Keeffe, 1887-1986
American artist.

To dance is to be out of yourself. Larger, more beautiful, more powerful. This is power, it is glory on earth and it is yours for the taking.

—Agnes de Mille, 1905-1993
American dancer and choreographer.

Life beats you down and crushes your soul, and art reminds you that you have one.

—Stella Adler, 1901-1992
American actress and acting teacher.

With each painting, I felt I was closer to unveiling a piece of the cosmic puzzle.

—Hilma af Klint, 1862-1944
Swedish abstract artist.

THE ARTS

HARDWIRED
HERMIE MEDLEY

I woke up this morning wanting
to knit a scarf, a russet scarf
with fringe. This was no casual wanting
but a smoking flame of need, the kind
I used to have when I was pregnant.

Then I'd knit blue baby blankets
for days while a tiny embryo floated
in my briny inner sea, throwing off
my hormones and filling me
with strange, quixotic longings.

Well, I can't blame it anymore on babies,
the way I get demented
every now and then, write poetry all night,
take up the ukulele, plant fourteen pots
of amaryllis bulbs, dance the tango
by myself around the living room. When
this morning's urge to knit grabbed me
by the throat, I went out in a downpour,
purchased yarn and needles for a scarf,
a russet scarf with fringe.

FAR FROM POETRY
JACKIE ZOLLO BROOKS

There'll be no poems today,
not with this fog, nor
as the humidity oppressively
advances, and especially not with
the financial advisor coming to explain
in her smiling voice all that has transpired
with my finances.
She is so careful, so honest, so fair
but she might be speaking Slovakian
for all that I understand or even care.
Next come the graphs—oh no, not
the graphs—what can they mean when
they sway all over the page like outlines
of shivering, shaking mountains?
The upward climb means positive gains, I think.
The plunges are miserable: disasters sliding
down in smeary tears of black ink.
But let me stay quiet;
let me look alert because my financial advisor
is taking me to lunch as she does every year
after I decline her invitation to a lovely cocktail party
for her many grateful clients.
Imagine such a group, rubbing elbows,
discussing assets and properties.
I'm not like them,
I couldn't be.

I never owned anything until my mother died
and suddenly, I could buy a car.
(I paid for it in cash. Well, there you are.)
Once I met these folks, sipping Manhattans,
crunching crackers and cheddar cheese.

They looked happy.
I watched them
mingle and chime,
never dreaming what a thrill it is
to pay one's rent on time.

HOW MUCH FUN CAN ONE PERSON HAVE?
JACKIE ZOLLO BROOKS

What if anyone knew?
Knew what I did
when no one was looking,
when no one was around,
when I am all by myself
which is most all of the time
because I live alone.
Would anyone be surprised to know
how much time I spend
doing a whole lot of nothing?
How much time I spend just looking
in wonder and joy at my flowers?
Or listening to music half the day?
Today I heard Rachmaninoff's
"Rhapsody on a Theme by Paganini"
on the radio. The announcer told us
someone once said to play this took:
"fingers of steel, a will of iron, the heart of a lion."
Did Rachmaninoff think that when he wrote it?
Does anyone think anything at all when writing,
painting, composing? What if anyone knew what
an artist thinks about at any given moment?
What would anyone think if he found out
an artist is—almost always—in touch
with the unconscious?
Would the person be dubious
or might he be frightened
or even wonder what's down there
deep in the unconscious mind...
or worse still, don't wonder at all?
What if anyone found out
what I am up to when I am alone,

wrestling with my demons,
relishing my selfishness,
eating the last pickle in the jar,
not necessarily my best self.
Ah, well.
What if they did?
Would it matter?

From the Preface to Her Novel,
"La Vieja: a Journal of Fire"
Deena Metzger

La Vieja first appeared to me in October 2017, the way characters do, suddenly, a complete stranger, seemingly fully formed, if obscure. Writers' lives are composed of such meetings. She wanted a writer; I wanted a character. *Bashert.* If I tell it the way it actually happened, I was in Santa Cruz, California, to give a reading of a novel I had just published.

While I was celebrating the book, I was also disconsolate as I had no idea what the next one would be. The day after the reading, I sat down to write and La Vieja appeared. It was the oddest experience. I saw her, and, in a limited but very particular way, recognized her— she was La Vieja—no doubt, who else could she be? And also she was undefined. Exact and indescribable.

But vague as her appearance might be, the intentions she announced were extreme and daunting, and a writer—the Writer, she asserted—would inevitably be significantly affected by her, La Vieja's, choices.

I braced myself.

In the past, in order to write what had insisted itself, I had had to master fields of knowledge and history, astrophysics, Mayan cosmology, climatology, the Conquest, and more. I didn't choose these pursuits. Characters arrived and I was obligated to accept them and their histories. Ultimately, they didn't choose their lives and so neither could I. Not fate but summons.

Naturally, I had to do research to see where they came from because I learned that every story is precisely rooted. From the beginning, writing and pilgrimage were linked in my mind because the sites I had to explore were saturated with human events and most often, tragically, conflict. The land bears the burden of our conflagrations and ambitions. When you are on a former battlefield or mass grave, you know.

When La Vieja appeared—she didn't knock at the door, you understand—the distinct consciousness, from which someone like La Vieja could emerge, entered my sphere with her, neither invited nor resisted, not only into the room, but into my mind which rearranged itself to accept her perceptions.

You know, in some ways, she is like a spirit. Maybe that is true of every character who inhabits a writer. For me, the writer, to transmit to you, the reader, the very essence of a character, I have to embody her and allow myself to be formed around what is most essential.

La Vieja was always precisely who she was, and, in another moment, she might appear differently in every respect. She appeared short, then tall, muscular, then svelte, seemingly fragile, then surprisingly sturdy, and was of no identifiable ethnicity, religion, race, culture, nation. She spoke English but you wouldn't say she was born in Cornwall, New Orleans, Bombay, or Brooklyn, but that she spoke the way you spoke, whoever you are, and so called no attention to herself.

In the beginning, our connection was tenuous. I attributed it to my inability to grasp her story well enough to write it and my inability to dismiss it and go on to another. A writer's classic dilemma. But here is the mystery. When La Vieja came to me in Santa Cruz in 2017, she had announced herself as a recluse. I was intrigued but could make nothing of it.

I was preoccupied with my life, with teaching, with the increasing urgencies of our times and, I suppose, with worldly business. I should have known, but nothing prepared me for such understanding, that when a character presents herself, she is an autonomous being and may not be ignored. The second time she appeared, I succumbed.

La Vieja had decided to take up residence in a Fire Lookout in the Sierras in California. She had entered solitary in order to see and intended to remain there. She wasn't planning to return to ordinary life, to being blind, the condition she maintained, in which most of us live.

She ensconced herself immediately in the story she would be living, as if having birthed her, manifested her, it nevertheless contained her; she had emerged from it and remained within it, her dwelling and her fate, without there being any contradiction between the two. It was a story which required solitude to be fully realized—that much she knew. This is what else she knew, or thought she knew: though she had left human society, she was not detached from human life. To the contrary, she had come to solitude for the purpose of investigating the times without obstacle or impediment and maybe, in ways she couldn't imagine, some good would come of it for all of us and for the future. What if anything the story would reveal was one objective. That the story would exist was another.

This later she assumed was realizable, if dependent upon me. Then circumstances changed. All our circumstances. Many things had happened in the more than two years since we had first met. Global warming has proved itself to be a misnomer and climate change is rapidly escalating toward climate dissolution. Wildfires blaze everywhere, also floods, tornados, and drought. Extinction is rampant. Global agitation, physical and spiritual. A few heartbroken and unshrinking observers of what is have begun to consider climate collapse as imminent. Some people petitioned for the rights of trees, rivers, mountains, so they could be protected and some of us agitated for the recognition of the crime of ecocide.

Then Covid-19 appeared, a spectre, a plague, another warning. La Vieja got my attention when she entered my studio again. This time, she spoke in a common language, in a way I could not fail to understand. Her appearance was a rebuke, reminding me that I had failed our accord. She had come, she said, to alert me. Also, she was going to sequester herself at the Lookout for the rest of her life.

La Vieja was not anticipated. Nor was the text that began appearing on the page, a text I seemed to be writing while simultaneously, or after a second's delay, reading for the first time, not as if I had just written it, but as if I were a reader discovering an unexpected plot line in a book by a familiar author. I followed it, slowly and carefully, wary, letting it unfold and more than often dismayed as I became completely lost in territories and characters that I did not know but couldn't abandon. Every sentence a surprise.

It is unnerving to discover that this text, which began years ago and which I have never fully understood but could not abandon, is exactly for this moment and these conditions. After great scrutiny of one's life and the manner in which we are living, possibilities appear: Live every moment as if this is your last moment to act on behalf of all life, not only your own, not only your species. When all life flourishes, may yours flourish as well. Through such a prayer, our species might align again at last.

* * *

Tonight, April 8, 2020

Because an old woman is making a toilsome effort to live alone, utterly alone, in a remote area near the crest of a rugged, uninhabited mountain not yet burned to ash in the recurring conflagrations. We are aspiring to see, to see the sweeping range of what we must grasp, we must grasp, of our precarious circumstances, human and non-human, organic, stony and inanimate.

When the certainty of a future for our species and all species is in question, when the past's bedrock assumptions of eternity are turning to gravel, and everything, everything, seems like it is coming to an end, I say with a slight nod to laughing at myself, that this book to the contrary seems to have a future in mind. Why say this? Because it wants to exist in and for a future. La Vieja, who is seemingly without any wanting, wants it.

This text is seeking its own precise completion, to be manifest in this specific present moment. For present moment has its own particularity and this one has been born out of the horror of what we have done to the world.

The human species is jeopardized, we have menaced all life. As a consequence of so many beings having gone extinct, the human is now suffering common jeopardy whether by chance, retribution, or revenge.

We are destroying everything through our passion to dominate while to our confusion a very littlest one is taking us down. We do not know if I or you or the species will survive. We hope our ways of life that are so cruel, so rapacious, will undergo the necessary and anguished transformation for Life to survive. This is the challenge. How dare we resist it? How can we fail to take it on?

Who is asking this?

La Vieja is asking this of us.

Oh, there is one more thing.

Fire.

81

ART
NELLIE WONG

Approaching old age with a cleaver
Murder certainly is not my intent
Stretching arthritic fingers a daily endeavor

The dance on the chopping block beckons seizure
Creating a tango of firmament
Garlic and onions pungent creatures

Fingers grip the handle of wooden texture
Command the hand with wild-orange scent
White hair bequeaths attenuating features

Old devil years weep and sing with pleasure
"Tiger near my body" causes no accident
Allowing Qi to flow with timely measure

Approaching old age creaks with more than gesture
Wrestle or wrangle with hours well spent
The art of aging takes work and leisure
Walking the picket line for ample pleasure

EIGHTY ONE YEARS
NELLIE WONG

For Flo on her birthday, October 28, 2019

Eighty one autumns arrive, butterflies wing across
Islands and lagoons
Gauging her life, gathering
Her art
Touch
You and you the many
O the bodies at Tiananmen, shots and tanks
Nesting not her wont, her brushstrokes not
Ephemeral   instantaneous   the rain the rain
Youth meander
Youth unfurl their lives
Entwine her eyes
Across her fingers the body whole
Remembering   living   a witness in
Story   in unhurried song

SILVER ON ICE
NELLIE WONG

Serenity arrives when you least expect it. Calmness persuades the sheen of silver, a flower garden against a night sky. You drink coconut water, thinking: ah, beneficial to your health two evenings before your birthday. Ice cold, the bay shifts, influencing sand dabs refusing to be eaten. Silver is not aluminum, consciousness a storm of wakefulness. To dream in oceans of stories, listening to echoes from rituals, ancient and new. You write to capture essence, a fast runner on ice.

METALS AND ME
LYNDA WATSON

It was 1966 and I was 26 years old when I took my first jewelry class at Cal State Long Beach.

A number of decisions I had made in my late teens and early 20s had led me here. I decided not to attend the university that my father had chosen and primed me for, instead completing an associate degree in commercial art at a community college. I had worked doing production art at a greeting card company until the lack of creativity drove me out. I had married and then divorced a very nice man because I wanted to make art instead of babies and ended up at Long Beach State because it was close, cheap to attend, and had a great Art Department. I needed to be surrounded by art people—my people!

I had been tempted to take Jewelry before, but had been scared away by rumors! From the start, the class felt different than any class I had ever taken. It was a serious discipline, involved a steep and extensive learning curve, and had a long and illustrious history almost everywhere but in the U.S. The program at Long Beach was several years old when I began taking classes. The professor, Alvin Pine, was just a few years older than me and was fresh from a Fullbright in Germany. Colleges and universities that had Metals Programs were almost exclusively taught by men who were either European or European educated.

Those of us who had strong, extensive art backgrounds struggled to assert our creative urges early on, but found that making art with metal came from learning and doing more and more—and it was eventually what we made! What is known now as "Art Jewelry" had its beginnings around this time.

The classes took more time, more commitment, more physical involvement, and more patience than anything I had ever done. It became clear as I took class after class that it was a discipline that selected its own practitioners. It was hard and demanding and simply not for everyone. I loved it like nothing I had ever done before.

The Art Department at Long Beach in the 1960s was a loose and friendly place. Those of us who were serious art majors were mostly from working-class families and were forced by economics and proximity to share housing, food, and transportation. The lower income side of Long Beach provided inexpensive rentals and plenty of thrift stores and used tool outlets. We shared everything. Financial support was always an issue. I dealt with it by living very frugally, selling the few valuables I had retained from my marriage, some work-study at the university, and becoming a partner in a shop/workshop with some other metalsmiths where I took commissions and sold some of what I made.

When I made the decision to pursue a graduate degree, my future path became quite clear. There were only a few colleges and universities that offered graduate programs in metals. After a short stint at Rochester Institute of Technology, I decided to stay at Long Beach where I had established myself as a jeweler who made art.

Most of my women friends left school at this point to get married or start K-12 teaching careers. I was the only woman in the metals graduate program at that time and I quickly realized that it was very important for me to make really good work.

In graduate school we also became more aware of the emerging art jewelry field and the people who were making important and interesting work here and in Europe. We also made contact with graduate students and faculty at other institutions and shared occasional visits, conversations, and photos of work--as much as was possible in the pre-digital era. There were women in situations like mine in a number of the programs and I knew their names and the work that some were doing. I was a little older because of my pre-jewelry background and may have been a bit more militant and clearer in my understanding of required behavior, but we all conformed. Like me, these early friends did not marry or even become involved in lasting partnerships until their careers were well established. Only one had a child. Casual relationships were OK as long as they didn't interfere in any way with doing our work. It was very important to keep making good work and lots of it, and to be showing it in museums and galleries regularly.

The Society of North American Goldsmiths (SNAG) was established in 1969 by a group of men who were university metals educators. My women friends and I became professional members and attended conferences each year beginning in the early 1970s. They were valuable casual events held mostly on college campuses, and several of us started meeting each year prior to the conference and every summer in Vail and Minturn, Colorado, at the Summervail Art Workshop. These times spent sharing dorm or hotel rooms or living in tents and working, eating, and learning together created permanent bonds. It has been over 50 years since some of us first met! The Master Metalsmith honor that I was given in 2022 has gone to five women who were part of these early friendships. Two were at the opening of my Master Metalsmith Exhibition.

In 1970, my Long Beach professor recommended me for an opening at Cabrillo College--exactly what I had been hoping for--a community college on the ocean! The job involved developing an Associate Degree Metals Program and a Crafts Program. I was interviewed and hired immediately but was asked at the interview if I intended to marry or get pregnant. I said I had no plans, but my boyfriend did move to Santa Cruz with me!

I spent 25 years teaching the Jewelry/Metals Program at Cabrillo College and retired in 1995. After retirement, and during the Covid pandemic, I have hiked, walked, and talked with an interesting group of people every week. We range in age from 58 to 91. The largest part of the group is involved in one way or another with art, but we have been brought together primarily by our desire to explore our amazing local surroundings on foot.

We share the minutia of daily life. We talk about aging issues, the difficult search for a place to live in a horribly expensive community, replaced knees and hips, the health and well-being of children, and of course, Covid and the vaccine.

I am a natural beach-comer, having lived very near the ocean for most of my life. I have collected beach detritus from all over the world. Some parts of my collection have already made their way into my work.

My work, regardless of media, is about my life: good times, bad times, new experiences, travel adventures, friendships, and celebrations. All of these are attached to places in my memory, and those places suggest the images, shapes, and surfaces that manifest themselves in my work. From Burma to Turkey to my own backyard, life happens in places.

In the fall of 2019, I received a letter from the Metal Museum in

Memphis, Tennessee. This is the only museum in the United States that exhibits, collects, and celebrates the work of jewelers, metalsmiths, and blacksmiths exclusively. I was informed that my name had been placed in nomination with other metalsmiths for the honor of being selected Master Metalsmith for the year 2022. While being the Museum's Master Metalsmith is one of the highest honors our discipline bestows, it also involves demanding responsibilities: the production of an extensive retrospective exhibition (mine had 89 pieces of my work), an accompanying catalog or book, lectures, demonstrations, and other activities presented by the Museum, and a trip to Memphis for the Exhibition opener and the Museum's big fund raiser, Repair Days. Those who wish to remain in nomination present resumes, images, and other required information, which is juried by all past Master Metalsmiths. One person is chosen nationally to represent the Museum as Master Metalsmith each year.

I was notified in November of that year, 2019, that I had been selected for 2022. The very difficult task of selecting, collecting, and preparing work to show and to include in the catalog (representing over fifty-five years of making) began the year I turned 80. It was clear that this would be the largest, most inclusive, and most important project of my career, and that both the exhibition and the book needed to confirm that. My work has always been about my life, so both are biographical; telling my story with the art I've made to describe and remember it.

Now, at 83, I am both reaping the benefit and paying the price for the life I chose to live. I have never been good at self-promotion and never cared too much about my status in the metals field. I have always just loved having the experiences and making the work. So, when I was selected to be Master Metalsmith, I was both totally surprised and deeply gratified. Suddenly, museums and collectors are interested in acquiring my work and I'm hearing nice things all around.

At the same time, I don't have the children and grandchildren that are so important to many people my age. My sister's early death left me very close to two delightful nieces and their families, even though they live out of state. I have many long-standing, close, and important friendships in Santa Cruz, so I lack very little!

Lynda Watson's Jewelry
Top: Pink Barnacle, *Bottom:* Charcoal Faces
(see cover art: *Looking Back*)
Images courtesy of rrjones, photographer.

UNADORNED
WILMA MARCUS CHANDLER

Northern California Powwow dance competition—
winning dance

The drummers, a wide circle of serious men,
hunch over the shaman drum.
Each holds a beater of leather and wood,
chants high and fierce,
wails the stories and prayers,
as she, almost 90, enters with a shuffle,
in her sturdy black shoes and housedress
and begins her dance.

Each footfall sends up flares of dust
from the dancing ground. Her legs lift, knees bend,
support-hose wrinkling around the full ankles,
her right elbow is crooked and the old, brown plastic purse
swings from her wrist, secure and rhythmic.
No beads or feather fan,
not Fancy Dress, not Jingle Dress, no woven shawl,
just her calm, heavy body, her long, gray braid.

She is dancing her domain to the unwavering thrum,
the rise and fall of the recitative.
And when her arms open wide,
the old dress sways into the wind.
The drummers' voices thin to birdsong.
All those who have gathered are silent in gratitude.

She flows from right to left
and again, right to left, right to left
like a river, like a mountain
descending to meet the valley below,
dancing all the seasons, all the years,

dancing the births and the passings,
in praise and in reverence,
the gritty dancing circle a dais,
the handbag a talisman,
her braid, the sole adornment, shining silver.

THROUGH STEVE'S WINDOW
WILMA MARCUS CHANDLER

On a visit to Missouri—6:00 AM

Here, I am the only one awake,
waiting for a light to pop on
in a nearby house, a car to start,
a neighbor to walk the dog
or fight the cold and start a run.
Porch light illumines the cul-de-sac, lawn,
a thin cover of ice over everything.

Steve's window has twenty-four squares,
four divisions of six, each square
a perfect little painting of its own.
In another life I might have wished to be an artist
to capture this space and every change in the light
as though each brought a memory and answered a need,
or an artisan who worked in the painters' guild
learning to grind and mix the pigments,
to discern which were basecoats
and which gave shadow or glint.

The sky turns from gunmetal to dove gray
and I think of my father, dying too young,
never needing glasses, his smokers' cough.
I think of my daughter
taking her son to school a thousand miles away,
and here, in Steve's quiet front room,
two pale chairs, two bleached pillows,
a low table with a vase of dried leaves.

In another life I would have wished to paint all this,
the colors, textures, things most holy and lasting,
as though each were the final thing I might ever see.

A WOMAN WILLING TO POSE
JUDITH FOX

—after Van Gogh's *Portrait of Madame Trabuc*

You wrote your brother that the warden's wife
was a *dusty blade of grass.*

A woman *resigned to her fate.* Vincent, that was cruel.
Still, models in the asylum were scarce

so you turned your brush, directed your easel
toward the woman's receding chin,

hair bound and knotted,
faded black dress fastened up the front.

And you painted the pink geranium
secured to her corseted breast. But did you see

Jeanne Trabuc—those lips that might have
upturned as she tucked into a buttonhole

the fragrant blossom—
a hardy flower from the asylum's garden.

I want to know more about your little-known sitter
so quickly dismissed—

step into the room where it happened, watch you
add pigments of cobalt blue to your palette,

hear the *insignificant* woman confess
how lovely it is to dress up. Sit for a minute and breathe.

NATURE

OLD WOMAN WALKING
KATHERINE WILLIAMS

County Clare, Ireland

Remember this fine mist that forms a scrim
between the hills that lead to the vast
flat white that hides the neighboring sea.
Remember the comfort of the ordered stones
that cradle this one lane road—each a headstone
for the nameless hands that hauled and split
and arranged them into balance.
Never forget how spider webs appear and appear
the closer you lean in, till the whole wall shimmers
with glistening silk, and fragile hammocks
hang from rock to rock and sparkle,
even beneath this shrouded sun.
Will you remember the insistent
gravitational force that pulls you away from the wall,
across the path, past the chuckling birds that lace their way
through blackthorn, past even the blazing campanula,
to a small protected field where two cows lie in ruminant silence,
their calves leaning against them?

THE MOON'S GLAMOUR
JEAN NORDHAUS

The moon's glamour is all reflected.
Under the dazzle and glow,
she's simply stuff and rock,

a ravaged heap of varicosities
and proto-dust blemished
with footsteps and trash. Spare her

the telescope, the magnifying mirrors
that reveal her folds and craters,
crooked teeth and odd discolorations.

Don't set your lens too harshly.
Practice faith, even credulity.
She's not the main act, after all,

but the attendant to the planet
of a secondary star in a galaxy
out on the edge of the universe.

When she puts on that gown of light
and glides across the sky,
gracious as a goddess or a queen,

give her a round of applause.

ONE THING
MARILYN ROBERTSON

One thing about a rabbit, or the moon,
is that they don't waste time fretting about
what to do with the rest of their days.

They are living them, one after another,
those tidy packages of hours with their beginnings,
their middles and their ends.

Rabbit, hopping along a path through woods,
into briars and out again without so much
as a scratch on its soft jumpy body,

and Moon, sailing across the infinite ocean
of sky, spilling her poetry of light into
every window she can find.

FALL RETURNS
JUDITH FOX

They stand in swirls of snow, the doe and fawns.
Snow descends and settles

and still they stand. The doe, deep breathing
through her keen nose,

might be recalling the shifting scents
of an October day when leaves were separating

from their branches
and the meadow staged a tumble of white clover.

Our window clouds. Shrouds
the snow, fawns and doe, the woods beyond.

After winter's thaw, after spring and summer
when fall returns and spotted fawns

are yearlings, will you still remember *deer*
is what we call those rose-destructive lovelies—

an echo of *dear*, your word for this woman beside you
whose name was once alive to you as *self*.

THE POLITICAL WORLD

Lion-Woman's Mane
Fereshteh Fatemi

Do you hear the roar of Lion-Woman's mane blowing in the wind?
Face to face with the storm of false beliefs,
With a broken back under the weight of being bullied
Her hands tied with the chain of religion.

The heavier the pressure, the readier she is
For freedom, she is ready to lose her head
But her Will is stronger than all the bullets.

Do not play with the mane of the Freedom Lion!

Excerpt from "A Revolutionary Memoir"
Barbara Joans

The rock misses my head by just a few inches, and I leap back laughing. Mary and I stare in wonder at the damage. Oh, why did no one think of this before! Oh shit! We start running. Neither of us is very fit and here we are running from the cops. Pigs, we called them. In that far away time, all cops are pigs. We stumble into an alley that we know leads out to Bedford Street and home. Mary plops down on the stoop and starts to giggle. Is this the way for a revolutionary to act? I giggle too.

I live in the luxury of a first floor, toilet-in-the-hall, railroad flat apartment. Small must be beautiful, because at 600 square feet, this place is the only home I will remember all my life. The only one I will ever love. My whole life happens here.

Everything in my life can be traced back to Bedford Street. A place I shared with my children, with each of my six lovers, several sequentially, and several in polyandry, and all my political companions. The place first mellows with jazz, then sings with English folk ballads, then jumps with political folk songs, and finally crashes and soars with rock.

First the intellectuals, then the socialists. Hard on their heels comes the Free University of New York, the red squads, the cops, and the narcs. Women's Liberation chases all those upstarts out and brings in its own kind of madness and transcendence. On the very toes of women, come the hippies and freaks and communal living.

My days are filled with childcare, my evenings with classes and my nights with study. I am obsessed; I love anthropology. I want that degree very badly. But I know not to crack open even an article during the day. The children are too distracting. While Davie is in play school, I take Howard in his little stroller to the cafes that line the village streets. These coffee houses make up a good part of village life. I hear itinerant singers, fresh from the hinterlands and filled with hopes. They play for handouts. Every time the hat is passed around, I remember always giving Bob Dylan a dollar (a lot of money for me to give) at the end of his songs because I feel so sorry for him. With that voice, I was sure he would end badly.

This was the era of sexism so pervasive and so demanding that teachers considered it natural to oppress women. It wasn't even considered oppression. According to my college teachers, women did not belong in college. The most outrageous example of this belief and behavior occurred every Friday night when Dr. Cerf, my philosophy teacher, held class in his living room. He did not allow women in his home. Since I was a student in the class, and the only girl, I had to stand on the porch and listen by the window while he lectured. Women reading this today will think they are reading about a strange land in a strange country hundreds of years ago but this was taking place in the mid-1950s.

For most of my young, wild days, the fear of pregnancy looms over everything. No one gives any sympathy and indeed, in that era, if a girl decides she wants to sleep with a man (the words were girls and men then) she is seen as responsible for whatever happens. The man might chip in some money for an abortion, but it is up to the girl to do everything else. When proof of an abortion can put you in jail, this is a very scary thing to do. I am one of the lucky ones. I do not have to take that long bus trip to Pennsylvania to the one kind, safe doctor who will help women and not kill us. But I do help other women take that bus trip to get to him. I run an off-the-cuff abortion referral service out of my home for many years before the laws change. I am forever grateful that I never had to use my own services. By the time I need an abortion, the laws in New York City will have changed, and thankfully I can get a legal one.

While I never defined myself as a rebel, there are times when others chose to do so. To me, rebel merely means doing what you wish even if your culture says no. It is going your own way especially if that way is against the grain. You choose a different way to behave. It may not be easy but at least, in America, it is still possible. Most of the time. To rebel is to look at the culture and say, no, no, not me. I do not choose to follow this path.

Quilt made by 100-year-old Grace Linn showing several books that have been banned in Florida. She brought it to a school board meeting in Martin County and spoke out against book banning. She compared Florida's actions to Nazi Germany, saying "I care about this community and our country." *Sheila Nevins, in her 80s, made a documentary after learning about Grace Linn called* "The ABCs of Book Banning."

No Red Diapers For Me: A Late-in-Life Encounter With Socialism
Sheila Carrillo

The first time I recall hearing the term "Red Diaper" was in 1998 when an octogenarian friend told me about a soon-to-be published book that she was featured in, *Red Diapers: Growing up in the Communist Left*. I was intrigued with the label red diaper baby and in awe of her lifelong, unflinching struggle for peace and justice that included tear gas and a jail cell at the World Trade Organization protest in Seattle when she was well into her 90s.

Recently, I was re-introduced to the topic through a community discussion of the book, *Red Letter Days* by Sarah-Jane Stratford, featuring three elder Jewish women educators and activists in my community. As a Jewish, left-leaning political-activist peer, I began wondering what had led me to socialism and radical activism, given that I had been raised in a polar opposite social/political framework. My father was an unrelenting patriarch and a rabid anti-communist.

So, at 81, I find myself digging deeply through family history and memoirs to uncover my political legacy—focusing on my father because, true to the times, my mother wasn't allowed much self-expression. Given my radically un-red diaper upbringing, how had I come to be viewed—of late—as an elder leftist political activist and writer?

At the time my parents met in a Jewish enclave in New York, they were both Democrats. But when in June of 1939, Roosevelt refused port of entry to the German ocean liner St. Louis with its 937 mostly Jewish passengers, forcing the ship to return to Europe where more than a quarter of them died in the Holocaust, my father was justifiably enraged. As he pictured Jewish refugees being handed death sentences by the Roosevelt administration—with the claim that they might be spies and were a serious threat to our national security—my father grew bitter, and in his bitterness and bullheadedness, he became a lifelong—and increasingly devoted—Republican.

My birth year, 1942, was a desperate and painful time for my parents and American Jews. Hitler was at the height of his power, and information was being widely circulated in the American press—confirmed by the U.S. State Department—that Nazi Germany planned to murder all the Jews.

Three years later, my parents picked up and left their beloved New York to be near my very ill grandfather in California. They must have been broken-hearted and anxious about leaving their roots, families, and livelihood.

What I remember of that first year in a trailer park in El Monte is crouching to draw circles in the hot dusty earth to play marbles with other black-eyed swarthy kids like me. I also have a disturbing memory of being called a dirty Mexican.

Going through a stack of my dad's yellow legal-pad letters, it dawned on me that a valued part of my life—my passion for justice, political engagement, and steadfast determination to right wrongs—has a direct thread to him, as does my proclivity for attending city council meetings and writing editorials and letters to the editor! Having paid him little attention over the years, I am grateful to have learned of his political passion.

His letters often mentioned the weight of anti-Semitism. To drum up construction work, he'd spent much of his time in his early 20s "knocking on doors up and down Madison Avenue—that wasn't easy for a Jew in those days." And among his news clippings, I learned he was referred to as a "local hell raiser at the city council."

My own hellraising began in my forties when I was hired as a bilingual aide in the school district where my brown-skinned children—whose dad was Mexican—had been schooled. In the course of my job in this rural mountain community in Santa Cruz County, I was shocked by the blatant racism I witnessed.

Through their writing and our conversations, I learned about the pain and hurt my students endured: a Korean boy's eyes filled with tears as he showed me how kids pulled at the corners of their eyes to taunt him, and my brilliant Iranian high school student talked about kids shouting "camel" at him as he walked by. Never having discussed racism with my two children, I learned from my adult son how uncomfortable he had been when his soccer team would drive to the South County farming town of Watsonville for soccer matches, and he was subjected to snide racist remarks about the Mexican teams.

Recalling my four-year-old self in El Monte and the antisemitism my parents had faced, I was enraged and energized, but lacked community or experience. Determined to promote diversity and inclusion, I sponsored a high school Diversity Club. We produced campus events celebrating multiculturalism and pressured the very traditional music teacher to transform the annual Christmas program to include educational presentations and ceremonies honoring Chanukah and Kwanzaa. I obtained grant money to put on multicultural programs at high school assemblies and to produce bilingual weekend programs for the greater community.

In time, I discovered a San Lorenzo Valley parent/teacher-founded group called The Community Equity Committee, and no longer was on my own. We teamed up to present a community-wide Prejudice Reduction Workshop and not-so-gently nudged the SLV district office to hire a Black anti-racism trainer to lead a workshop with district teachers and administration about the not-much discussed inherent racism and white privilege in America. I see now that I was beginning the daunting lifelong task of examining and unraveling my own white-privileged Jewish upraising.

My dive into socialism began when I was an elder, in my seventies. Triggered by my disappointment with Obama's misguided policies and my growing loathing and distrust of the Democratic Party and inspired by Bernie Sanders' socialist platform, I became a member of the Democratic Socialists of America.

Through DSA, I encountered social issues and movements that both educated me and compelled me to write commentaries to educate and inspire others.

Initially, I was introduced to CAHOOTS, a model alternative to police, ambulance, and fire department services to address non-violent crimes both on the street and in homes. The transformational potential of taking non-violent crime out of the hands of armed police struck a chord in me. I dug in my heels and launched what became years of strident advocacy and public education. Through writing, public presentations, and meetings with city and county, I pressed for

24/7 alternative emergency mobile response teams, countywide. At this writing, I'm still agitating.

I began participating with a group dubbed "Love Boat," delivering lunches, tents, first aid/hygiene supplies on Sunday mornings where needed. A vision and hope for a future transcending the greed and inhumanity of Capitalism began to take root.

An astrologer once told me, "Capricorns are old when they're young and young when they're old." With perhaps a decade or two left in my "youthful" octogenarian life, I look forward to continuing to write, to share revolutionary ideas, and to strive to shake up the status quo.

Part Four

HOW I GOT HERE

A strange thing is memory, and hope; one looks back and the other forward; one is of today, the other of tomorrow. Memory is history recorded in our brain, memory is a painter, it paints a picture of the past and of the day.
—Grandma Moses, aka Anna Mary Robertson Moses, 1860-1961
American folk artist.

The past, the present and the future are really one. They are today.
—Harriet Beecher Stowe, 1811-1896
American abolitionist and author of *Uncle Tom's Cabin.*

If you love your life, you also love the past,
because it is the present as it has survived in memory.
—Marguerite Yourcenar, 1903-1987
Belgian-born French essayist and novelist.

One cannot and must not try to erase the past merely because it does not fit the present.
—Golda Meir, 1898-1978
Ukrainian-born Israeli, Prime Minister of Israel,
labor minister and foreign minister.

WHY I REPEAT MYSELF
JOYCE KIEFER

I love the way a good story lingers on my tongue like a caramel
    dissolving slowly.
A nugget that could be chewed and swallowed, done with
    but is better savored
    by the tongue which picks up the elements—
sweet, salty and the bitterness of burnt sugar.

I know that friends, kids, grandkids have heard before and before:

    How I threw my hiking boots at a bear that tried to open my
        backpack—and lived
    How I had to walk everywhere in the rain – Mom didn't drive.
    How I glimpsed the race track with families clinging to the fence,
        waiting to be interned—Dad told me not to look.

Everyone knows the kicks I got on Route 66 on a family road trip
    in the early '50s.

Perhaps I've grown senile in my 80s, forgetting who has heard
    which story,
    Does it matter?
That person has probably forgotten it
    or listens politely while stirring up a favorite tale of her own
To savor as we share
The communion of old friends.

Notes From A Geriatric Diva
Maude Meehan

Sunday afternoon, radio playing rainy day music.
It's been pouring for days. I've been going through
old photos of friends, relatives, past gatherings
teasing a kaleidoscope of joyful and melancholy recollections.

This one, a song-filled celebration with new friends
taken more than thirty years ago, when we moved from
the east coast to Santa Cruz. We found ourselves among
a varied mix of long-haired poets, artists, surfers who
welcomed us by helping to unload our belongings.

We were starting a new life from scratch among
the gentlest people we have known. To one side
of our cottage lived earth mother Apple, and Spirit,
a sandal-maker PhD, with their dog Cannabis and a cat
called Silly whose whole name was Psilocybin.

They brought into our lives a host of friends,
some of whom have moved away since Santa Cruz
became a pricey place to stay. And I won't forget those
three dear gay men friends, lost that first epidemic year
to AIDS. First Little John, and Larry, then Daniel,
gifted concert pianist, the last to go.
I still miss them, miss their wit and loyal friendship,
still have red ribbons in a drawer.

Now and then I run into some of the old crowd, now
upright ordinary citizens. No longer driving beat up vans,
but SUVs, working in real estate, or silicon valley.
Tie dye and patches abandoned, along with dreams
of a caring, kinder world.

Oh, here's a photo, wide angle, of my younger brother's
wedding reception, more than forty friends and family
captured clapping and smiling as the cake is cut.
Now only five of us remain – myself, my older brother,
two cousins and the bride, now nearing eighty and
long since a widow.

Days spin to weeks, and months, then years, like
pinwheels in high wind, and so much still to do.
I make small foolish bargains with capricious Fate.
Barter for time to finish this or that, knowing full
well how she springs swift surprises.

At any rate I see time's at its usual tricks,
and I must tidy up this heap, reminders of a
rich plum pudding past, and ease back into my
daily world, a strange well-meant arrangement
called assisted living. I've already missed this
afternoon's Activities: Armchair Aerobics, Nickel Bingo
and good old Benjy on the Banjo. Well, if I hurry
I can make it down in time for Cut-Throat Dominoes
and dinner.

FLATTERY
MARGIE KERN-MARSHALL

When I left France, I brought back a Citroen Deux Chevaux. I named it Flattery, because like flattery, it didn't get me anywhere. It was the '60s. As a student it was daisy stickers and I danced happily along in Manhattan Beach to sensitivity trainings and free-love fests. Flattery had turn signals that were actual metal arms that stretched out on command. She had headlights that you could adjust up or down or sideways. Her canvas top rolled down manually like a sardine can being opened. She was easy to park. Two people could lift her, one in the front bumper, one at the rear, and then drop her into any tight parking spot. There were problems. Flattery was vandalized by war hawks as the daisy stickers were peace symbols of the anti-war movement during Vietnam. Also, she was illegal in the U.S. because her windshield wipers only worked when the car was moving, slowly when you went slow, and faster as you accelerated. The metal arm signals were off-standard. So, I accumulated many traffic tickets. The worst thing was the road-rage she caused. Because of her slow acceleration, passengers had to walk alongside her when she climbed steep hills. When traffic lights turned green, cars behind me honked and yelled when I couldn't rev up fast enough for them. But among Flattery's many admirers was my husband-to-be, Lee, who was a former race-car driver, and that's how we met.

RUBBINGS
BERNICE RENDRICK

At first light
I rub the pale inside
of my elbow
in a small effort
to continue
the flow of blood
that makes my life go on—
though with a little less
force downstream,

The light is brighter
in the slits of the blind
like eyes unbandaged
to see this room again
where I wake
to the batik curtain
and the black Rose Gonzalez pot
from Santa Fe
my husband gave me one anniversary.

Memory rubs the inner lip,
illuminates the deep carving
which cuts a wound
that breaks open
and I must relive
the hospital's phone call
at dawn on his death day.

But this vessel heals
even as it hurts
so squat and dark
with its hard finish.

Pie Making
Bernice Rendrick

My aunt carved
a vine of flowers
for vents in the pie crust.

Grandmother wove a trellis
over sugared blackberries
gathered that morning.

Mother braided
the scraps
into cinnamon strips.

My pie crust falls apart.
I patch it with clumsy palms.
We eat it like those broken wafers,

bland and dull, placed
on our tongues at church.
Restless, I'd turn

to a warm ray of sun on the pew
or consider my sins
in the rose flower

on the stained glass window.
I knew then, I know now,
each thing our hands make

or our souls find
where light has signed it
saves us, forgives.

THE GOOD CRYSTAL
SHIRLEY RICKETT

One night when the children were young,
I entered the kitchen from a walk to cool down.
Beneath my feet shattered crystal among
remnants no longer to ring with sound.

I had entered the kitchen from a walk to cool down.
The house was quiet except for tears about.
Smashed goblets and flutes for wine with no sound,
stunned at the sound already gone out.

The house quiet except for tears about.
My two little girls in their white nightgowns
stunned at the sound already gone out,
my son like a dart raced with no sound.

My girls held each other in little nightgowns,
tried to come to me but their feet were bare.
From a closet my son raced without a sound.
My husband appeared with a suitcase like a dare.

They tried to come to me but their feet were bare.
My home became a house full of things and sand.
My husband appeared with a suitcase like a dare.
He left with his own agony in hand.

FROM A HIPPIE TO HER MOTHER
LAURIE CORN

Excerpt from *The Half-Built House on the Hill:*

> *The family of four lives in a half-built house with faux ceilings
> and walls and, over time, the woman comes to accept the critters
> that share their space, especially the ten thousand flies that were
> the nemesis of her life; she comes to peace and acceptance, in a
> Buddhist way, of the "hippie" culture of the '70s.*

I love these sounds
  tinking of a spoon against a cup
  bleating of the goat down the hill
  hum of the car coming home

I made a cake this afternoon
When I poured brown sugar for the frosting
  a mob of ants scurried out in all directions,
but they left me just enough—two-thirds cup

Forgive me, Mom
We have learned to share our home with
  field mice in the shelves
  scorpions in the garage
  baby frogs on the kitchen sink
  bees, bats, ten thousand flies
  and ants in the sugar
But they have left me just enough
  keeping the sugar loose
  as earthworms keep the garden

It is fly season again

but I have become a Buddhist on this hill
and when I see a fly drowning in some apple juice
I fish it out to drag its wings dry

I could sit here for hours at the top of the hill
  listening to the wind
  the laughter of men down below
  throwing horseshoes
gazing at the sculpture of stark white clouds
against the deep blue infinite sky

YOUR WHITE KNIGHT
LAURIE CORN

—for my mother

Excerpt from *The Two Gents and I:*

> *My father, a widower, moved to Santa Cruz at age 80. In his last days, I lived with him at the home of his brother Paul in Santa Barbara.*

My father pushes himself out of his easy chair,
stands for a moment, and wills himself across the floor.
Later this evening he will sit on the edge of his bed,
      with fumbling fingers unbutton his shirt
button his pajamas
slip under the covers
and rise in the morning
to start again.
In the hallways of my child's mind, it is 5:00
and he is striding up the front walk after work,
my mother peeking secretly
through the tall narrow window by the front door,
her hands clasped, and she is saying:
"Just look at him. Isn't he handsome?"
And I would ask again how they met
and she would answer in her sing-song voice:
"He was riding a white horse and found me sitting on a green hill."

Mom, if you are still watching
through your tall secret window,
tell me, give me a sign that I am doing this right.
Your white knight is now my charge
here in the sweet dusk of his life.

How do I take care of a knight
who is an old man?
I am no good at knitting sweaters.
I am worn from worry that he will fall,
break his hip, choke on a bone.
And still, sweet lady,
he is the bravest knight
who bears his pain in measured steps
and tries, and pushes on.
I can touch him
I am here
but I am not his Guinevere.

THE MYTHOS OF MY CHILDHOOD
LAURIE CORN

Excerpt from *The Half-Built-House on the Hill:*

I think it is in the passing of the seasons that I am Home. When all else fails, there are the autumn leaves. There is the frozen pond in Ottawa Park. There is the budding dogwood tree in the front yard. There are June Bugs at Lake Erie.

My childhood is an eternal kaleidoscope of seasons turning and turning. A young girl is darting perpetually around a backyard fenced by lilac bushes, catching lightning bugs in a jar until it is a glowing lantern in the dark, and then letting them go, to rise up and hover like tiny helicopters in the thick, muggy sea of night.

Turn the kaleidoscope—and she is raking fallen leaves with a wide-spreading rake into huge piles, then running and landing with her brothers and sisters in the crashing, sinking softness. Turn again—and she is sitting on the window seat of her knotty-pine bedroom looking down on the first snow of winter, everything marshmallow soft and round: the brick windowsill outside the breakfast nook, the street curb, the mounds suggesting garbage can or rock or tree root. And then, on that first warm day of spring when she can leave her cardigan sweater at home, she is walking up the tree-arched street to Old Orchard Elementary, feeling light and breezy and hopeful.

I was born a child of wartime. The horrors of that war did not touch me, except as undercurrents and whispered voices. What I see is my young parents embracing in the hallway of the red brick bungalow. I see my mother in her tan, gabardine slacks raking the Victory Garden and my father, home from work, striding up the front walk, cold air surrounding him like a cloak, as he reaches up to place his hat on the coat closet shelf.

My father was a tall, Gregory Peck, prince-of-a-father sitting for all eternity in his easy chair, pipe raised to his mouth. My mother was a fountain of beauty and goodness standing at the clothesline in a flowered, wrap-around dress—a Norman Rockwell painting. My mother had a moonface—high Russian cheekbones, white powdered skin, eyes as blue and sparking as an Indiana summer lake, and a smile painted Revlon "Cherries in the Snow." I see her moonface beaming down at me, as seen from a small face looking up. It was her moonface that seemed to promise: 'Everything is all right and will always be all right.'

My romantic fantasies are rooted in the '40s: in the dresses, the hats, the heroism, the music. I remember those war years in a cozy, comforting way because in my family, everything was all right and would always be all right. That was the premise and that was the theme.

In the post-war years, neighborhoods spread, and businesses grew like mushrooms out of piles of scrap iron. There were fortunes to be made, and even if you had a small family business such as my father's jewelry and watch repair company, if you invested wisely, you passed "go" and collected $200, and the houses were bought and placed like Monopoly pieces on square lots with a Buick in the driveway, evergreens in the front, and a fenced-in backyard with a dog. There was no rush or urgency to life. One year expanded into the next as the kaleidoscope of seasons turned.

There are no more beautiful streets in all the world than the streets of Old Orchard where I walked to school every day. Not in Beverly Hills. Not anywhere. The branches of great leafy trees formed vaulted archways over the streets. Stone castles lined the boulevards, with turrets and leaded glass windows. My brother and the other boys on our street were the Knights of Drummond Road, each with sword and shield, and they fought regularly over Suzie Hanson, the blond, blue-eyed one who lived next door.

In this perfect world you could count on the blue spruce trees to be laden with snow, tobogganing in Ottawa Park, road trips to Washington at cherry blossom time, June barbeques, cottages and row boating at Pottowatome, Sunday school, piano lessons, Broadway musicals in Detroit. There was everything. Everything. Nothing was left out.

It is difficult for one not to conjure up some gothic serpentine spirit ready to spiral up out of all that goodness, some hidden awfulness that was repressed, but truly there was none. No wonder my Aunt Rose asked me, "How can you write a memoir? You had such an idyllic childhood." True, I am not Sylvia Plath or Anne Sexton—no suicidal poet. I had no lusty uncles, no grandfather with wandering fingers. I have lived through no reign of terror, escaped no European tyrant in the dark tunnel of night. I'm sorry. I apologize for my sweet, harmonious family, for the brick house on Drummond Road, for the birch tree Mom planted in the front yard, and winter snow walks, and June barbeques. I'm sorry.

AT EIGHTY
MAUDE MEEHAN

This morning, I tuned out the news,
unplugged the phone
opened the back door
inhaled delicious fresh
spring air, and wondered
who could ask for more

I couldn't help delighting
in the pecky sound of birds
out on the deck
plucking at mounds of lint
I'd saved all year from my old dryer

I always set them out
on the first sunny day
imagining nestlings,
cozy in fluff from
fuzzies saved all year

Why, only yesterday I had fun finding
Easter cards and baskets
for my grand and great grandchildren,
oh, and I treated myself to a CD by
Santana, that sent blood coursing
madly through my varicosities.
And furthermore, last night I had a dream
no nice old white-haired, widdy woman
is supposed to have, what's more
I thoroughly enjoyed it

So though my wild and woolly days are past

don't for a moment think
that you have heard the last
from this old lady, and did I
mention by the way that when
I heal and throw away this cane
I have on layaway a big red Harley?

MY MOTHER'S VOICE
JUDITH FETTERLEY

This past November I celebrated my 84th birthday. In July, Sara, my partner, celebrated hers. We like being in the same "grade" together, perhaps just a bit farther along than kindergarten. We are aging at roughly the same pace, have the same memories for music and movies.

Though we have no immediate plans to leave our large home and garden, we have begun to ask how long we can continue to maintain it. Sara fatigues at the thought of calling the plumber, the electrician, the snowplow guy, but I am still up for mowing the lawn and weeding the vegetable beds.

We have, however, agreed that it is time to start thinning and tossing. Last year we contacted a real estate agent to explore options. She talked brightly about the importance of being nimble, ready to move at a moment's notice when the right place appeared on the market. Nimbleness at our age sounded like a good idea. Sara chose to sort clothes; I chose to tackle my office closet.

My office closet contains several repositories loaded with "treasures."

Neatly preserved in tissue paper and claiming its own box is my tin animal collection, a reminder of my Canadian childhood and my own financial frugality. My parents gave me a nickel a week as an allowance. I still have the "bank" where I deposited my weekly nickel. It is made of metal, shaped like a book, and "Savings for Baby" is engraved on the "cover." Why get a new one just because I was no longer a baby?

I saved until I had the requisite $1 that would allow me to go with my mother to the store that sold tin animals where I could purchase the expensive water buffalo to add to my collection or perhaps a pair of polar bears. Each animal as it was brought home was carefully recorded by name and function in a registry that my brother and I constructed from heavy-duty construction paper. I look at these relics of my childhood now, battered, paint peeling off, legs missing, and think, "I remember each one when it was new and beautiful. I can't let them go."

In my former vanity case, part of a luggage set given to me at my high school graduation by my mother's best friend, are two gold medals, one for each year I won the Indiana state-wide Spanish proficiency contest. I can't let these go: they represent an alternate career, a path not chosen but deeply desired, even regretted. I have a gift for learning languages. From German language operas and a first-year college textbook, I taught myself enough German to pass the foreign language exam required for my Ph.D. in English literature. I longed to study German to proficiency and, with three languages at my command, become, perhaps, a translator for the United Nations. I did not follow that longing, but I can't let go of the reminder that I could have lived a different life.

In its own box inside a large cardboard carton labelled "Earl's Pearl Tomatoes" sits my mother's favorite pen, beige-bottomed and silver-topped, the one she used to write all her letters, the one I found for her one day on the floor of the bank where we went to open my first account when I got my first job.

At Sara's urging—she was sorting her clothes, what was I doing to achieve nimbleness—I reached into this carton one gray November day, pulled out a handful of envelopes and took in, once again, my mother's handwriting, perfected from her lengthy study of the Palmer method, clear, lovely, and simply there. The plan was this: I would read a letter, enjoy it, and then toss it.

The first group of letters I pulled out were written to me during my two years in Boston as I was coming back to life after four dreadful years of college. I took a job, first with the Harvard Business School, then with the American Friends Service Committee. Reading these letters I could recover, in my mother's response, my love of Cambridge and Boston; my delight in learning that as long as the columns matched, the books were deemed accurate; my commitment to social justice work; and my decision to leave that path and enter graduate school.

The second pile of letters, some in envelopes, some loose, were written twenty years later, at another turbulent time in my personal and professional life. I was ending a ten-year relationship to begin another, this time with a woman with two young children. I had left my marriage before Earl and I had children, and as a lesbian of a certain generation, before the prevalence of sperm banks and sperm donors, children of my own were not an option. I was terrified, scared that I would fail at the job of mothering.

I was also struggling with a new direction for my writing, one that had the potential to derail my growing career. As a scholar of American literature, I had made a reputation writing about Mark Twain. I followed this with a book analyzing the sexism embedded in the form and content of our classic texts from the 19th century, all, of course, by men. Now I was going to explore what women were writing during the 19th century. I wanted to know if it really was "trash," or if the label was just another manifestation of the virulent sexism of the field. All this I could trace in my mother's letters to me.

I began bravely, prepared to read a letter, then toss it. I read the first letter and thought, I will hold on to this one for a bit, it contains an account of a conference my mother attended with me. I read a second letter, tossed it in the bag, then immediately retrieved it thinking, I can't throw away the memory of her bonding with my new partner over their mutual love of Maytag washing machines. I read another and learned from it why I had chosen to buy a particular cottage on a particular lake. And so it went. I threw away not a single one!

I couldn't.

The letters bathed me in her love. They let me believe I was a good-enough daughter. But it was not for this comfort that I stayed my hand. Nor did I hold back because her letters are full of memories and facts, facts that help me now to understand myself then, memories that enrich my understanding of my relationship with my mother.

No, it was hearing my mother's voice that kept me from tossing. Reading the letters, I could imagine her sitting on the couch across from my rocker, eating her favorite pecan and maple sugar scone, sharing her thoughts. It was my mother's voice, thinking, that I could not bear to toss.

In a different time, my mother would have been a professor and a scholar. She attended the University of Chicago, unusual for a woman of her generation, and majored in religion and philosophy. In my office closet, the one that contains her letters, I have her university diploma. It is printed on parchment paper and her name is written in Latin— "*Mariam Elisabetham Wilsdon*".

My mother never stopped thinking, questioning, wondering— how did the universe begin, what was the right way to live, what really constitutes identity? She was tough-minded, probing the stars and God and the choices I made with equal intensity and zero cant. Her mind in letters is the gift she left me.

I have put away the carton containing her letters, those read and those unread. I will be taking them with me if we move. As for nimbleness, I have turned to sorting clothes.

My Abuelas
Judith Ortiz Shushan

1. Reynalda

Grandma Reynalda's front porch screened in a space framed with slabs of rough-cut splintery wood. Screens began chest-high to a four-year-old and met the ceiling, and they were thickly woven with a tapestry of grape vines, probably older than Reynalda herself.

No matter how hot the day, how bright the sun, how dusty dry the New Mexican earth, the porch was cool and green and fresh and quiet. Here and there small rents pierced the leafy walls, hollowed by Reynalda so she could observe the world. They were not cleanly cut casements but places thinned to camouflage her spying.

"There's that Salazar girl again with her short skirt and her lipstick! She'll be in trouble one of these days...."

"Bah! *Again?* That Mrs. Padilla just watered those lilacs last night. What a waste of water! She should take that good care of her children..."

"*Look!* There he goes, *cochino!* His wife, *pobrecita*, she pretends she doesn't know that he meets some woman once a week at the Sinverguenza Motel. Men! That's all they ever want...."

Such was the running commentary she made on life outside the porch. She had been deserted by her bootlegger husband long years ago, left with eight children. Two died and all the rest, except for the baby, were sent by the State to orphanages—the boys in Albuquerque and the girls in Santa Fe—until she could feed them, or until they were old enough to work. Now, many years later, her children grown and gone again, from the green protection of her porch she lived on tidbits of other people's lives.

I think she meant her pronouncements to be lessons on life, but the only lesson I learned was that the adult world was a confusion of change—formless and unpredictable, one without pattern or design—where no one stayed put, nothing stayed the same, and nothing was what it seemed to be.

I sat many dark evenings in that porch so alive with its rustling of grape leaves and electric cicadas, listening with Reynalda to "The Fat

Man," "Blood on the Moon," and "Inner Sanctum," my eyes never leaving the green glow of the radio dial as all the terrors of those tense mysteries flew out at us, Reynalda, and me, and the porch.

I do know that I passed countless mornings in the porch, smelling Reynalda's strong sweet coffee—rich with Pet Milk—watching her plunk squares of yellow-gold cheese into the steaming cup and spoon them out when they'd melted, leaving fat grease bubbles sliding on the surface of the coffee. She'd suck up the cheese, fastidiously blot the stringy strands from her lips with a folded napkin, and read the comics aloud — "Mutt and Jeff," "The Katzenjammer Kids," "Nancy and Sluggo," "Alley Oop." Then she'd turn to the front page of *The Independent* and read to me the scariest news in the paper —war news and stories of violence and murder and assorted outrage, real-life echoes of the radio tales that scared us so deliciously.

Those times in the porch never changed for me. Even now, now that I know that life lasts longer than love, the memory remains clear and clean and strong, the one memory undiluted by merciless change.

No, the porch didn't change with time, but Reynalda did. Her back sprouted a hump, her brown body twisted in on itself like a winter vine, and her breath smelled like rust.

They tore the house down, right down to the earth, and I avoided looking at where it used to be. But sometimes, as I walked past with my eyes to the ground, I would see in the red dirt, relentless brown coils spiraling up through little bits of trash.

2. Eloisa

Although we were often together, my Granny and I never had a single conversation in words. We spoke to each other in pantomime —pointing, nodding, grinning, shaking our heads, throwing up our hands in bewilderment. Grandma Reynalda told me her stories, but Granny and I were silent together.

For a time, Granny took care of me while my parents worked. I'd go to her house after school and stay until my father came to get me. Her house was painted "Beaner Blue," the name white people gave to the bright color, the clear blue of the thin horizon line where sky and high desert met at dusk, that vivid blue color favored by Hispanic people and judged by *gringos* as garish and vulgar. They didn't know that that blue kept the witches away.

I felt still in her house, and safe. It was always quiet, dim with shadows winking from the votive candles burning in front of a carved wooden *Virgen de Guadalupe,* the air infused with incense. There was a tapestry above her bed depicting a Spanish cavalier serenading a *Señorita* on his guitar, she in a black lace mantilla raised high on a tortoise shell comb, leaning over the balcony and offering a red rose. Was she Eloisa in the Olden Days? I'd rest on her bed after school, stare at the beautiful pair, and make up stories about them. On her chiffonier were a pair of castanets. I wanted more than anything to play those castanets, but they were too large and useless in my clumsy hands. Made of some heavy black wood, maybe ebony, my father said, they were joined together by colorful strands of braided twine. Next to them lay a large Spanish tortoise-shell comb with an opal at the peak, and the black lace mantilla Granny wore to church.

One early September afternoon, sluggish with heat and back-to-school weightiness, I daydreamed my way to Granny's house. When I got there the house was locked and empty. I knocked. I kicked the door. I ran around the house, jumping up to peer in windows, but I never called her name. I searched for her in silence, then made my way home to wait.

My parents came home angry. I had worried Granny, upset her, she thought I had never come back from school, she had called the nuns, she thought something bad had happened to me, how could I be so thoughtless, what was wrong with me, she's old, she must not be upset like this.

When things settled down I learned that Granny had not forgotten about me, had not abandoned me. She was just visiting her *comadre* next door and had left a note on the screen door telling me to meet her at Señora Jacinta's. Her note, of course, was in Spanish. I couldn't read Spanish. I couldn't speak Spanish.

My mother wanted me to be successful in life; she cast her dreams in the outside world with me as the player. No Spanish meant no accent. And no accent meant no houses of Beaner Blue. But it also meant exclusion, isolation. Spanish was a secret language to me, a language of secrets, shutting me out and separating me from my own while shutting me into a private lonely world.

I'd watch Granny. And listen to her gentle voice. And wonder about her. She'd sit embroidering in her large easy chair, and I'd stand beside her, watching the beauty formed by those deft hands.

Granny Eloisa would hold my hands, smile into my face. Her eyes contained the mystery of myself—she, a living source of answers but denied me, separated by a tongue that was at once alien and, by rights, my own. My cradle tongue: Mute. We'd giggle. We'd roll our eyes at each other. We'd squeeze each other's hands. I'd smell her sap. One day I thought of a way to show her my devotion. Because of her dental problem, she couldn't crack her beloved *piñones*, so I decided that I would make a great pile of them for her as a surprise. I carefully picked the largest ones from the full gunny sack on the back porch, cracked them firmly but gently between my front teeth so as not to crush the oily seeds, and pushed my tongue into the cracked shell to dislodge them— a delicate maneuver requiring much patience and skill, since the seeds split so easily and keeping them whole was a challenging feat. I sat at her feet while she sewed, performing these steps over and over, pretending to eat the *piñones* myself but secretly removing them from my mouth to the growing pile in my lap, rubbing the spit off on my dress. What temptation! But I allowed myself to eat only the ones I'd broken or crushed.

When the pile was impressive and my tongue was sore, I scooped the seeds into my hands and presented them to Granny. I had no words to get her attention, to explain my offering; I simply poked her leg— covered in those thick tan stockings she always wore, rolled up in garters above her knee—held up my bountiful hands, looked into her face, and waited. She responded to my poke with her sweet shy silent smile and I thought I heard her heart exclaim, "A whole pile of *piñones!* Shelled just for me!" She formed her own hands into a scoop and I spilled the seeds into them. Comically she rolled her eyes at the sight, her face crinkled into a grin, and she popped several damp seeds into her mouth, naked gums crushing them into mush, savoring the oily richness as I watched her, thrilled at her enjoyment.

Her bright black eyes, suddenly serious, fixed me at her feet, something in them as urgent and as serious as life itself. She looked down at me and a deep silence froze the moment. Then, softly, she broke it: "Gracias." With aching absorption I stared at her mouth, her lips, her serenely quiet face, and in wonder I listened, and I looked for me, for myself.

Gracias.

RAT-TA-TA-TAH
TILLY WASHBURN SHAW

I'm cheerfully making my way
springing into each step gladly,
when feet sound behind, approach.

Quicken—remember then how when younger
I always sailed ahead –for instance with
my boyfriend, not really meaning to,
became his beacon light or bowsprit.
Face 4-feet in advance, caught up
with my own beat, in love with
the forefront.

Today still junketing along, while footsteps
ever closer soon pass me by,
the way they never used to,
find me left behind, still

Savoring my velocity, at a loss why
I'm apparently walking faster
much slower now.

EMPTYING AN OLD CLOSET
TILLY WASHBURN SHAW

     One by one
Things to get done with—
Reposition, toss, pass on to others.
They emerge in twisted clumps,
boxes that need flattening,
bubble wrap scraps, nests of ribbons
some still knotted, others carefully
ironed and rolled, ridiculous
how my time was spent in the past,
the lovelicks involved, my dwelling
on things, my savings…

All this to say goodbye to,
unwrap the fingers of, uproot
desire for.

Open Those Doors
Joanne Hale

I spent most of my life opening doors of opportunity that came my way. Be not afraid. If it was an exciting opportunity and could enrich me, I went for it. It led me to an amazing, fulfilling, and meaningful life.

Twelve days after graduation from college in Oakland, I was in Peace Corps training and three months later boarded a Pan Am flight for the Philippines. I taught high school biology and chemistry in Tuguegarao on the island of Luzon for two years, attended the International Rice Research Institute (IRRI) for six months while "Miracle Rice" was heralding in the Green Revolution, and became Peace Corps staff for 1.5 years while training new Peace Corps volunteers in rice production.

After my adventures in agriculture, I decided to pivot from education to agriculture and graduated from the University of California, Davis, with a M.Sc. in International Agricultural Development. There is nothing more satisfying than feeling passionate about your work! Next, off to Papua New Guinea (PNG) for seven years with husband and two young children and six months pregnant with the third. Initially we were volunteers at Puas on the island of New Hanover for three years and built a vocational school, dormitories, trained teachers, established food gardens, a piggery, and a chicken coup. This was an amazing submersion in a culture that moved with lightning speed from Stone Age to independence in 1975. We arrived in Puas in 1972, just when Michael Somare became Chief Minister of the country; we witnessed an exodus of expatriates as the Day of Independence grew nearer; and we remained to witness a peaceful transfer of power from the Australians to the people of PNG three years later. In our seven years we experienced life under colonial rule, self-governance, and full independence.

On our first island, we lived without roads, without food markets, and with only rainwater for our supply of water. The villagers were wonderful! We five all learned to speak in Melanesian Pidgin and the three children were completely incorporated into the lives of the villagers. They had never known the concept of danger, kidnapping, or hatred.

They had been surrounded by so much love and affection on all sides from everyone in the village. They could visit anyone and enjoy their hospitality.

There was no concept of growing food for selling. My husband attempted to introduce the concept and on the very first day of the market, one fisherman was trying to sell his fish for outrageous prices. It was all entertainment for the villagers; they did not take the concept of markets seriously. The lesson I took away was that one should first find out what people most wanted and then help guide them in that direction. My son, meantime, was patiently at the same market selling the peanuts which he grew himself to pay his tuition at Ungulik. He was utterly fascinated that by planting one peanut in the soil you could get 25-50 peanuts back!

My husband designed a weeding hoe which he felt would help the women who labored hours in their gardens. When I joined them once, they abandoned their new weeding tool and told me that they preferred to bend over and weed with their knives. It gave them time to relax and socialize. No one could see them when they were bent low in their fields.

We moved to Kavieng on the island of New Ireland for two years and then to Wewak in the East Province for two years. I conducted annual evaluations of the agricultural officers and found them to be utterly honest about their professional strengths and weaknesses. I was the only female on these trips. Women were not yet admitted to the agricultural colleges. This changed toward the end of my seven years in PNG.

From PNG, I moved to Sri Lanka as an irrigation agronomist contractor with the United States Agency for International Development (USAID) for a year with my children. After a year, I joined USAID as a Diplomatic Foreign Service Officer and was assigned to Bangladesh for four years. The children and I have many fond memories of our times in Dhaka and formed many close relationships which we still enjoy today.

The next step was in California. It was a year of acclimating all three children to life in America – their first time ever. What did I forget to tell them? When I left for Africa, all three of them were at UCSC and helping each other adjust.

My first assignment in Africa! A continent I learned to love very much. I developed a program which still exists today in Malawi. The "Small Holder Farmers" (SHF)—those with less than one acre of land —were allowed for the first time ever in Malawi to form tobacco marketing groups and sell their product on the auction floors in Kavieng and Blantyre —the largest tobacco auction floors in Africa. Tobacco accounted for 75% of Malawi's foreign exchange earnings and the government was loath to let the SHFs join the 2,000 estate tobacco growers on the auction floors. It was an intense battle on both sides, but today more than 90% of the tobacco sellers are SHF Marketing Groups. Their revenue is paid in US Dollars and electronically transferred to the bank accounts. This infusion of money into the rural economy fuels the entire country's economic development, as farmers buy bicycles and radios for the first time and bicycle/radio repair enterprises evolve in their wake. Families for the first time have sufficient income to send their daughters to school as well as their sons. Educated girls marry later, have fewer children, and engage in microenterprises which ensures that all children can attend school and apply for jobs and move off their small family plots. Education is the escape hatch to move out of their repetitive poverty cycle.

After four wonderful years in Malawi, I was stationed in Uganda for two years as the USAID Deputy Director and then to Nepal for 4.5 years as the USAID Director —a magical experience in the Himalayans.

From Nepal, I went to Uzbekistan for a year, as the USAID Representative and managed a $150 million portfolio: irrigation, trade, health, and agriculture. Next, I worked for the United States Department of Agriculture (USDA) in Rwanda, Uganda, Malawi, and Ghana on short term assignments. This was followed by nearly two years working as a contractor with the Bill and Melinda Gates Foundation in Ghana, Ethiopia, Tanzania, and Kenya to develop a multi-crop agricultural value chain assessment to increase food supplies and farmer welfare.

I then joined the Center for Food Innovation and Entrepreneurship (CFIE) at Santa Clara University and taught the "Feeding the World" course for seven years. I have served on the Board of Directors for Gravity Water, an NGO which provides energy-free, roof-top rainwater harvesting for drinking water in schools in developing countries. I continue to serve on the Board of Directors for Context Global Development which invests in agricultural and social impact programs in developing countries.

I have lived a most wonderful life and am deeply grateful to my three amazing, loving children who kept our laughter going and gave me the gift of four grandchildren who daily enrich my life!

Part Five

SEXUALITY, ROMANCE, LOVE

There is something akin to freedom in having a lover who has no control over you, except that which he gains by kindness and attachment.
—Harriet Jacobs, 1813-1893
American author and activist,
writer of *Incidents in the Life of a Slave Girl.*

When I write of hunger, I am really writing about love and the hunger for it, and warmth and the love of it and it is all one.
—M.F.K. Fisher, (Mary Frances Kennedy Fisher,) 1908-1992
The New Yorker food writer, American essayist, author of 35 books.

A woman in love can't be reasonable, or she probably wouldn't be in love.
—Mae West, 1893-1980
American actress, comedian, and writer.

To be in love
Is to touch with a lighter hand.
In yourself you stretch, you are well.
—Gwendolyn Brooks, 1917-2000
Poet and university teacher, first Black poet to win the Pulitzer Prize,
first Black woman to be U.S. Poet Laureate Consultant in Poetry.

It is a curious thing that when one speaks from the heart it is invariably in the worst taste.
—Ngaio Marsh, 1895-1982
New Zealand author, theatre director, and mystery doyenne.

Ingrid Bergman's Hat
Patricia L. Scruggs

At the airport, he parks near the elevator so the car will be easier to find.
We hold hands as we walk. "Just twenty-one days," he says.
Another quick kiss and hug before he turns toward the TSA line.

On my way back to the car, I avoid eye contact with others. No one
ever looked good in tears at an airport, except Ingrid Bergman.
Maybe it was the black and white. Maybe it was her hat.

I turn the radio to the jazz station and drive too fast on the way home—
my husband's car won't slow down. After midnight, I wake to rain.
It's cold. I miss him beside me. I picture him asleep

somewhere over the Pacific, noise cancelling headphones in place.
I get up, find the Casablanca DVD, wrap myself in a blanket,
push "Play," fast-forward to the last scene. I want to hear

Bogart say, "We'll always have Paris."
The camera cuts to Bergman. Her eyes tear up.
She's wearing the hat. She looks great.

ANNIVERSARY SONG
SYLVIA BYRNE POLLACK

Listen, love,
what I wanted to say
dissolved in this afternoon's
plummeting rain. Lord knows
we need rain but the timing
was off. No umbrella,
words written in chalk
on my hand.

Listen, love,
what I meant to say
has already molded—overripe
cheese, fuzzy peach in the back
of the crisper drawer.

Listen, love,
what I might have said
is in the pants press
I gave to Goodwill.
What I should have said
was festooned with blossoms,
garlands of fuchsia crepe-
paper petals.

Listen, love,
what I will say is
I'm heating the leftovers,
and supper will be
on the table at six.

No Words For It
Tilly Washburn Shaw

Such very old women.

At meals in the retirement home
they would make a signal others didn't see
then one would excuse herself
and a moment later the other
follow suit. This was how
they arranged to meet daily
for a moment down the hall
in front of one of their doors
and embrace. Unimaginable,
such a tender goodnight kiss
from two such very old women.

My mother snorted in the telling.
She was 88 and they were acting like schoolgirls,
ought to pull themselves together.

At this end of their lives—85 and 83—
their minds hardly reached anymore
to the rest of us, their ports of entry
closed to the large print and
louder voices with which we
pressed them. It was easier finally
just to give up on words
and loosen hold.
They had no other place to go to.
It couldn't happen in a bedroom,
needed to be done in the open
so as to mean right and put at a distance
the mind's other thoughts.

Untroubled about whom they loved
since life left them but a handful
of persons, they took whatever offered itself
and opened their needy hearts
humble and greedy both. You might
think it matter-of-fact but it was also romantic:
dreams hopelessly mixed in with needs
the way probably it always is.

My mother ended her story with
a surge of impatience: adolescent
crushes at their age! The others
followed her of course into laughter
eager to push away deeper
yearnings they were all now too old
and close to wanting
to avow.

HOLDING HANDS
TILLY WASHBURN SHAW

—for Maggie Berger, 10-29-92

I'd rather have you
living anyplace but in
a poem. Where
else, though, after
I saw you still breathing,
the large almonds of
your lids closed, hiding
eyes that no longer jumped out
to exclaim crossly,
your bare shoulders thin under
a crisscross of tubes, mouth
plastered to a stick and another
black thing you noisily
breathed through.

No matter how
hard I tried, I couldn't
recognize you—27 years yet
I'd never seen you with
your eyes shut. Still it
comforted me to pull up a
chair and sit closer by,
your left hand in mine cold, but
as I held it
warmer.

Of course holding hands
is nothing we'd have
done living.

No matter
between old friends.

God Is Not My Man
Jill Ginghofer

A fury of white hair,
wisps of beard,
girth hoisting side to side
as he whirls, clutches air.
Beneath his white robe,
penis dormant but
balls hang and clang
as he rages, cheeks
bursting with
nothing is right.

The devil, on the other hand,
perched on hoofs,
spindly legs,
minces toward me.
He's interested.
He responds.
He couldn't give a shit.
You can say anything.
He muses on poetry,
likes good movies
reads everything in a flash,
makes careful suggestions,
and he's so thin
his erection looks divine.

TIL THERE WAS YOU
LUCILLE SHULKLAPPER

—For S.D.

The jazzy beat and bluesy voice sings birds winging and bells ringing
and the sound of her voice wails she never heard love all around her "til
there was you." Who was the you in her song, I wonder, was he real, and
I lean over to touch you in the dark, you are real, your body is warm,
one arm hugs the pillow in your thick fingers, the other dangles over
the side of the bed, your breath even, the tempo smooth. It is cold tonight, your bare chest, doesn't need a cover, and when I touch you, I
hear the beat of my own breath losing and finding love again, though I
need two covers, and I shiver underneath them, losing and finding myself again in dreams I try to remember in the morning, when you make
coffee, and I stumble around, and I know your covers are gone, but mine
are still there, needing warmth, needing you, but the smell of coffee is
the music all around, and though you kiss me, I want to be your pillow.

I watch you in this Covid all around, taking the paper salad bowl,
and filling it, with walnuts, and raisins, slicing the avocado you love,
and wait for you to leave, to exercise in your own studio, that you've
never slept in, and then I take eight pills, because of spinal surgery, and
I wish I had more spine, but I try, and taste the sweetness of cake with
my coffee, or sugared fruit slices, and clean up the crumbs I leave, and
the crunch of paper in Covid tempo, til there is you, and maybe a hug,
and sometimes I hear music when the covers disappear and I let myself
be loved, when we sip wine, in our matching indigo chairs, and you
pour it, into my glass, into me. We dance to this song, and you hold me
close. I breathe you in, and I am your pillow.

I am 80 when we meet, and there is music all around us at a dance,
and you and the music are one, from the moment when, you sat across
from me, making it easy to fall in love again, as though I always knew,
you and love are one, though it simply has begun, the habits of the

heart, never really part, what was there in your glance, that made me take a second chance? I was afraid to fall in love with you, afraid of fire, afraid of lies, afraid of long, and sad good-byes, your kisses startle, your touch confuses, I'm yesterday young, sparking old fuses. I hear the music, that tango, that waltz, dance with your virtues, glide over your faults, love when you're older, does somersaults. I see the birds winging, hear those bells ringing, and know there's love, in coffee grinds, in the sweetness of crumbs and crunch, in our bodies, touching. I breathe you in, and love's magical fragrance inhabits my soul, with a mind of its own, long sleeping on two pillows *til there was you.*

ANY DETRITUS
SHIRLEY RICKETT

can send you to rummage old photos, letters
to make a feeble charge at the past and send you
to the porch with its new cushions while you wonder
how long they will last in this heat, and the porch
of memory where the first kiss took place from
the softest mouth you ever knew, the night insects
holding off the breeze, a sweet breath of insistence,
these fragments, the least and most of memory.

So you find the pool, empty save for two other
aging bodies and you marvel at the surface net
of silver blue circles around you as they bend
and save each other, the palm tree green fingers
silvering into icicles as they flash in heavy sun
against a cloudless satin sky.
                              You think on
your childless home with the latticed fence
your husband made to keep the pup in and out,
and those cushions, and how many days, hours,
years you may have left. Don't think
on possibilities. These things sustain you
and him as you reach for each other
to embrace your lives at the end of another day.

PAINTING THE WRINKLES
ALICE FRIMAN

That's what a setting sun does
to the face of the sea, frost
to November's desiccated leaves.
That's what the politician does
to his record, what the family
photographer saying *smile*
enacts with a click: a sprinkle
of fairy dust—a pair of epaulettes
for the shoulders, a little flash
for the shrug.
        But let's talk
serious: I need something for
my face beyond soap and water—
a cover-up. a lotion, a shmear.
You bend to me, assure me
I'm still your plum pudding:
a Band-aid effective as a kiss
on a hurt when what I need
is a tourniquet.
        I know, I know.
Next step is sackcloth and ashes.
I give up, you convinced me.
It's ten o'clock in the morning.
Outside, the sun flexes its muscles.
Come, let's play doctor.
Lower the shade. Examine how
the shadows paint me young again.

A LAST TIME
JAN HARWOOD

I'm a seriously old woman
but I still get the urge sometimes, you know?
And last night, the time seemed ripe;
lying in my bed, a completely sexless mystery beside me,
cat sound asleep and no one else about—I decided to give it a shot.
My fingers felt a bit rough on my dry and delicate clit—
but I thought that might help,
as determination, pressure and friction have always worked fine in
  the past.
(I believe it was less than a year ago when I achieved multiples
  of joyful pleasure time after time,
savoring the multiple smiles on my age-weathered face.)
But last night there was no joy
Not even a damp premonition of delight—
Only some, like, hopeful discomfort—
and eventually, the cat woke up—
miffed by the persistent shaking of his
peaceful bed, he jumped down with a soft growl
like a disapproving maiden aunt.
I guess it's okay, since I never thought I'd be here this long;
and pleasures still come crowding in
through my eyes and ears and palate;
memory constantly lavishes me with a symphony of love, losses,
triumphs and failures—good stories all!
It's strange to be so abundantly alive in this time of chaos and
  suffering,
when it's more clear every day that the center cannot hold.
And last night I realized that, as there has got to be a first time for
  everything,
there must also be a last.

THEY
JAN HARWOOD

When she became they,
love soothed any shock
even tried the vocabulary
resulting in strange neologisms
When there was talk of injections, surgery,
when the silvery voice deepened and dark hairs began to sprout
love admired the new tattoos on creamy skin,
held out its arms and held they tight.

FAREWELLS WERE BEING SAID
HENRI BENSUSSEN

Farewells were being said—*so much fun; it's been years; we should do this again*—as our former writing group gathered up empty containers and left through the gate of Tam's new and very tiny home.

"I'll stay and help clean up," I said, and began collecting dirty plates for the outdoor sink. Tam was the youngest in the group. A few lines appeared around her dark brown eyes, but her tanned face wasn't as wrinkled as everyone else's. She wrapped up leftover cheeses, put away grapes. If only it were as easy to put away disturbing images and emotions tossed up by an overly stimulated brain. Would I be happier if I weren't worrying about my middle-aged daughter away on an African safari with a side trip to Zanzibar? Why go to Zanzibar for cats, Thoreau had written, when they were found in abundance at home in Concord?

Thoreau had an answer for a lot of life's major crises, like deaths of friends, and how to live in a one-room house. My apartment in a senior community was larger than Thoreau's cabin, and a great deal larger than Tam's latest experiment in home ownership. Her house looked to be nine feet long and six feet wide, and reminded me of a gypsy wagon. She had invited our old writing group for her tiny-house warming.

We were a group divided by age, by those with children and those without, the divorced and widowed and still partnered. We'd lived each other's lives for over thirty years, from the time we had formed, in 1984. The Monday Night Writers. I had recently divorced, coming out as a lesbian after a long marriage. Tam, the other lesbian, had regaled us with her adventures of when she was picked up as an exotic prize by a woman in an upscale suburb. There had been one death, the oldest, at 90, of the original group, and now some of us were approaching that age.

Over the years, everyone had managed to publish: books, poems, articles, stories. We were all still committed to writing, and linked through email. Lately, most of my writing had taken the form of poetry; I'd been sending out manuscripts for a full book of poems, so far without luck. My partner had died the year before, and I had a lot of free time, much needed for my current memoir project. I was going to spill out all my secrets before dying, like going to confession with a rabbi, where we would argue over the meaning of "secret."

Returning to the outdoor kitchen, we said goodbye. I hoped we would all meet again; I didn't want to lose connection with this group of women. We'd been through so much in the years we'd been together, before we began retiring and moving off in different directions.

As I drove toward San Francisco, I remembered that time in the 1980s when I divorced and "came out." It was odd to phrase it that way, since I'd never considered myself closeted. I was so excited over my future, starting over as if I were eighteen again.

After my partner's death, the first question from friends had been, "What will you do now?" I began a list of all the things I could do, freed from care and living alone for the first time in over thirty years. My brother and his wife invited me to an Alaskan cruise. I started with that, joined a newly-formed LGBT discussion group, put myself on a schedule of weekly hikes, and registered for the BOLD Conference in Vancouver, BC, an annual event for "older" lesbians, in the fall. Maybe I'd meet someone at the dances they held.

A lot of books have been written about love affairs full of passion and pain. I had loved my partner, and also had to tolerate some of her painful behaviors—the more difficult side of her personality as she entered dementia that most friends, I hoped, didn't know about. I suffered during that time, and suffered still, now that she was gone. What I missed most in this new state of being was someone close to be affectionate with. So far, the only friend I had given a hint to about this idea, a woman of my age and circumstance, had answered that, after years of love adventures with numerous women she now felt herself, unlike me, "too old" for such things, what with various ailments, and anyway, she looked nothing like what she'd been in her youth, only, it seemed, a decade ago.

I had recently reread the story of the escaped campfire Thoreau started that destroyed quite a bit of the woods around Concord. Thoreau was blamed, and tried to make the best of it, though it would be six years before he was able to settle it in his mind. Seeing the blasted landscape recover its life with new grass, new flowers, he wonders why he too, like the burnt woods, couldn't send out new leaves in spite of his "searings

& witherings." Feeling seared and looking quite withered, I willed myself into the burnt landscape of my changed life, hoping for a bit of greenery. The family cruise had been good, and also the BOLD conference—dancing every night, learning stand-up comedy, exploring Vancouver, meeting lesbians from Canada and other parts of the U.S. But I'd not met anyone to be close with, nor at the LGBT discussion group, though I'd formed friendships there.

If I had a garden… but all I had was my third-floor, south-facing balcony, too hot to grow anything; the one attempt I'd made, setting out flowers in pots, had been eaten overnight by some animal. Laura Dassow Walls had recently published an in-depth bio: *Henry David Thoreau: A Life.* "His longing for a deep connection with the land," she writes, "would make *Walden* into the great American fable of alienation, regrounding, and rebirth."

I couldn't mimic his life, his intellect, his commitment to an ideal, but I could appreciate and follow him. My reclamation would mean finding a new place to live that allowed for a deeper connection with the natural world. It would mean finding someone to share my life with. When you let yourself love someone you learn to be more human. When that person is no longer alive, you learn how to continue on without them, and also keep yourself open to love if it happens to float toward you in its many guises.

I glanced down at my shoes, as I thought this, and decided I really needed a new pair. My toes would be a lot happier if they were allowed the freedom to spread out a bit. Also, that there's a lot of crap on the ground that one has to watch out for. So maybe one's goal should be to notice more deeply, not rushing through but contemplating the world. Exiting the freeway, I met a stop sign and stopped. Thoreau would have done the same. I felt him with me as I continued onward, at a slower pace now that I was nearing my neighborhood, noticing trees along the street, the park where kids were playing at one end and a homeless encampment took up the other. A lesbian weekend at a retreat center called "Enchanted Hills" was happening soon. I had a hopeful feeling about it. Hilton Als had written that "hope implies intention." I was brimming with intention, overflowing with hope.

WELCOME TO EIGHTY
JUDITH COHEN

They tell me I don't look like 80—actually, I'm not yet, but soon will be. What are numbers? They can't measure our lives. I try to live in a continuous present. My fifty-year-old daughter as well as many friends think I've lost my mind. But I've agonized for months, and I've considered this decision very carefully. Yes, I know I'm hurting Max, my husband (my second husband, but we've been together for more than thirty years).

Last year Max and I rented an apartment in Venice; it had been our dream—to spend a month in our favorite city. What I love about Venice: no cars, narrow back streets, and bridges carrying you over canals with antique palaces reflected in the simmering water. To Henry James it was "an orange gem resting on a blue glass plate." I imagine poor Shylock walking the backstreets forced into money lending by anti-Semitism; ancient rooms where Portia might have argued her case. For Thomas Mann's dying Count, obsessed with a beautiful boy, it was half fairy tale, half tourist trap, but irresistible.

We met Flora through some English friends. Her glorious apartment overlooking a canal had high ceilings, glittering chandeliers, and old paintings. There she held salons like a 19th century grand dame. Flora spoke English and Arabic; she'd been a translator and though not wealthy herself, she had good connections. She'd sublet her grand residence from an old Italian aristocrat forced to go into care. Flora hosted lovely dinners. We spent many evenings with her guests; such compelling people—poets, diplomats, scruffy artists. Nobody cared that I was old. Everything in Venice is old—that's what draws us there.

When it was just the three of us, Flora and I talked into the night, as she lounged on a velvet chair, her silk garments flowing, her long silver hair swept over her shoulders. I was enthralled by her story—how she'd grown up in an immigrant household in New Jersey, studied art history and linguistics and became a curator, then a translator, the lover of many men and women. I could only guess her age—but as I said, age doesn't matter. Max often fell asleep on her couch. Though he's younger than I am by a few years, he's tired all the time. In the last decade or so, he'd lost his curiosity—all zest dribbled away. Flora was so attentive to me—eager to read the stories I'd published so many years ago. I felt reborn with Flora— my life shimmered again, illuminated by her brilliance.

After we left, Flora and I wrote emails, almost daily—I like to think of them as handwritten letters but alas, those days are past. In her eyes, Max and I seemed like a mismatched pair. "You are so much deeper than he appears to be. Why spend your remaining years waiting to die?" She invited me to return, without him. "Your companionship would complete my life. Let's spend the time we have left indulging ourselves."

When I told him I was leaving, Max thought I was simply taking a trip and would return. Then he begged me to see a marriage counselor—then he wept. Nevertheless, he helped me empty our house and sell our car. I found him a small apartment closer to his son, a small task he couldn't manage without me. Max clung to me at the airport. Yes, it's true, I filed for divorce and flew to Venice, to Flora. It's not exactly sexual but thoroughly sensual: pungent tastes, delicious scents, glorious music. I will celebrate my eightieth birthday with her.

Postscript from Max: I got an urgent call from my soon to be ex-wife. She was in the hospital having broken her hip after stumbling and falling on the Bridge of Sighs. Her girlfriend refuses to care for her— "she's simply not equipped." So, I must meet the flight and bring her to my place. I'll care for her until she heals. Will she stay or return to Venice? I hope I can persuade her to stay with me here in the frigid north. I suppose I'll bring her some flowers—lilies, her favorite. Her birthday is this week. We shall see.

RITUAL
JOYCE SCHMID

Like the Charlton Heston movie
where a mutant peels
her face-mask off to show her
twisted features to her god, I bare
my own time-wounded body to
the cold December sheets you've
tried to warm for me. I speak
the words, you say them back, still
hard for you.

Here in the lull between two battles,
one we've won, the other we're about
to lose, we bumble through the
ritual of youth, more slowly
now, more careful of our
bones. We've learned
each other, practicing innumerable times
along the path to clouds and rain,
a comfortable storm
with flashes of incendiary light.

PUT THE KETTLE ON
MYRA SHAPIRO

Tea? I've begun to ask each evening
partway between dinner and bedtime,
and he's begun to answer *Yes*.

It's an old marriage. We're beginning
to merge. Just this month, arms aching,
I began following his morning routine,
the hot shower so my arms move
with ease. In his case it's knees.
Last night I wanted to sit next to him
as he sat on his side of the bed, simply
to chat a bit about the Middle East,
the peace talks he's been listening to—
and what else was important today?

I wanted to hear his excitement before we went
to our separate sides of the bed,
our particular pillows and the good sleep.
It's all just begun, the new year. March
is here, and we're living it.

LOSING HIM
ANGIE BOISSEVAIN

The great blow fell on her
when he knew he had to go
and quickly left then,
and all she carried, years of it,
went with him,
and all he carried
stayed behind with her:
orchard, manuscripts, anxious friends,
telephones pealing and pealing,
ringing her loss as church bells
would have done before—
and his final poem, Amen, lodged
in her spine and belly,
words saturated with his presence,
echoing already from another world.

WORDS
MYRA SHAPIRO

Bastrop. Say you are not wed
To words; you are
17 years old, a freshman
Invited by the best dancer

To go to Bastrop, a town of
Parks not far from Texas U.,
With him and another couple
For the night, and

You don't turn to say
What a weird word, Bastrop.
You want to go with him,
Cook out together, and

You don't know the other
Girl and boy will go into a room
Alone, you don't know she won't return
To you, leaving you to room with him—

This is 1949—you only go so far—
It's understood—3rd base—not all the way—
Suddenly he's home. Your marriage
Bastrop born. 70 years later

Bastrop pops up in your head
Why? you ponder—he knows
Your story, only he's no more
Alive, your husband, son-of-a-rebbe,

Your Gemini to his Scorpio, the man
Who acts, no questions asked,

The woman open, who turns
To Rumi's words:

Lovers don't finally meet somewhere.
They're in each other all along.
And soon you'll lie in a plot
Next to him. Bastrop.

Part Six

The Body

The body says what words cannot.
> —Martha Graham, 1894-1991
> American dancer and choreographer.

Everyone says you were beautiful when you were young, but I want to tell you I think you're more beautiful now than then. Rather than your face as a young woman, I prefer your face as it is now. Ravaged.
> —from *The Lover by* Marguerite Duras, 1914-1996
> French novelist, playwright, screenwriter,
> essayist, and experimental filmmaker.

The doctors told me my hearing would get worse if I continued swimming, but I loved the water so much, I just couldn't stop.
> —Gertrude Ederle, 1905-2003
> American Olympic swimming champion.

After a certain number of years our faces become our biographies.
> —Cynthia Ozick,1928-
> American short story writer, novelist, and essayist.

Now the girl runs without a care,
Both arms held high above her
head—At last
She is chased
Only by her destination.
> —Nabaneeta Dev Sen, 1938-2019
> Bengali feminist poet, novelist and educator.

80 is the new 2—you might not walk very well, you could fall, you don't have all your words, you spill things, you sometimes wet your pants...
> —Dena Taylor, 1941-
> American poet and editor.

DEGAS' BATHERS
PATRICIA L. SCRUGGS

I step from the showers in the women's locker room
covered with an oversized towel that conceals

scars on my right breast, stretch marks
on my abdomen, broken veins on my legs.

The women around me emerge in colorful wraps
or comfortably nude. All ages, shapes and sizes,

they remind me of Degas' studies of bathers
stepping into or out of the tub, turning and bending

to towel themselves. These women are every bit as beautiful.
I want to take out my charcoals and sketch them—

their heads, balanced on delicate necks,
the complexity of their shoulders,

the curve of their glutes,
the unguarded hollows behind their knees.

THE OLD BODY
ANGIE BOISSEVAIN

Is a road trampled and overbuilt,
is a train pulling into every station,
is a garden intensely dug and fed.

The old body is a lopped tree,
a riverful of ruined tires and dozing trout,
a radio with too many stations.

Looking up, we're all blue sky inside.
Casting down our eyes, we're rocks in our own path.
Our breath, our yellow teeth, our crevices and cracks,
fold in and fade.

We're opening thunder's door
and dissolving as we pass through.

SELF-PORTRAIT AT 80
ANGIE BOISSEVAIN

She doesn't know who she can be any more.
She's in a daze of desire for more of everything, when
she can no longer manage very much at all.
She's stubborn and angry about this.
She knows what she wants, and she doesn't want
this other thing especially this not-knowing.
She can see she's supposed to accept
new limitations with grace, and she can't.
Always strong and able,
there's no reason to stop.
Except for all these new reasons that have long
medical names and unfortunate effects,
back, side, and frontal.
There are good reasons she can't walk well,
And hurts.
There are good reasons she tires easily,
She, hires doctors, tries
to overcome all of it.

SPINE
ANGIE BOISSEVAIN

Exquisite fixture, tough
backbone held its thick body,
framed the form, a temple
walking brilliant, prancing,
now gone small, it crumbles
looks like the letter C.
Looks like her mother's
and her mother's,
like rice field workers'
and sweepers' who used
short brooms.
Once shapely, fair,
she stands humbled
at too-heavy postoffice doors
as young men pass in
and out not-seeing her.

OLD UGLY
NAOMI NEWMAN

HAG (*looking at audience*)—You're out there, are ya? You know, it's not so easy to look at you. 'Cause when I'm looking at you, I know you're looking at me. And I know you don't want to see me. Come on, don't deny it. Let's not have any of that polite crap. You don't want to see me because I am ugly. Old and ugly.

You know, the other day, this fellow, he comes along and he starts up a conversation with me. And he says, 'What's it like getting older?' 'Older,' I said, 'older than what? What makes you think I know anything more about it than you do dummy? You've been doing it since you were born.'

Think. Since I started talking to you we have aged exactly the same amount, right? Right? Let me hear it, am I right or wrong? Right. It doesn't take a mathematical genius to figure that one out. So… how does it feel getting older?

Think. Most folks imagine they're getting smarter as they ripen. Then comes this mysterious moment, and all of a sudden the fruit is rotten. Folks expect you to smell bad, piss in your pants, or forget to button your bra. How come? How come? How many gray hairs do you need to slip out of the human race? How many wrinkles can you get away with before folks start talking slow, loud, and stupid at you?

You know, if most of you passed me on the street, you would either not see me or you would turn away if you did. Do you know why? Do you know why you don't want to see me? 'Cause I look like graves. I am bending down, back to the earth, getting ready for re-entry. Well, you see me, and you say, 'Won't be long now, she's going to drop dead. Lucky she's too dumb to feel bad about that. Lucky that's not me. Lucky I'm taking my vitamins.'

I'll tell you what. I'll tell you what. You put a picture of me on your mirror, on your refrigerator door, and on your checkbook, and I guarantee you a spiritual awakening in less that a month. Study me, study me 'cause I'm studying you.

All right, let's see what recycled this morning. (*picks up cut-out words, shuffles them and reads)*

"Rotten talks backfire   peace erupts the pentagon   joins the homeless."   That's a great haiku, don't you think? *(stands)*

You know, if you weren't so afraid of me, you could die laughing. You're going to die anyway, you know, you might as well get a chuckle or two.

AFTER THE SCHERZO
LINDA NEAL

if you want more / there's the sky to admire —Margaret Atwood,
"A Painting of One Location on the Plain"

I don't want a red lace dress, fancy hankies
shutters and doors that let the light in.

I want to live wild wave-barrel
surf to Zanzibar, to chocolate bar,

          bare breasted and bikini-bottomed.

I don't want what I have, crave the Ha ha ha,
and *shaka brah* of youth's innocence and rebellion.

But it looks like I'm settling for one new hip
a transplanted kidney, berries in a bowl,

       and rows of lady head vases on the shelf.

Memories of a wet-tongued dog humping my leg
float through my days like moths in a pantry, searching for light.

Forget memory—I get it why people's brains go south.
After the *scherzo* it's all *allegro molto,* a dance through shrunken options,

       ailments and waiting (for what).

SHAPES OF TIME
GLENNA COOK

I used to think my ankles
were the best-looking part of me—
slim as flower stems, with a classy knob
of bling sporting each side. Now
at certain times, say, a hot day in August,
they resemble two Bratwurst sausages.
My once graceful hands, fingers
slender and nimble, performed
with ease every task I assigned.
Now, enlarged, bony knuckles trap
rings, have trouble with buttons,
and can't open a jar.
My dainty rose-petal ears
could hear the softest whisper.
Now, grown like cabbages,
they no longer decipher lyrics of songs.
My heart, I'm happy to say,
with tough, bitter endurance,
weathered the times and improved with age.
It's etched with scars of grief, thickened
to protect, and so loosely assembled
that love seeps out through every seam.

Alice Neel standing next to her self-portrait. Neel was an American visual artist, whose career spanned from the 1920s to 1980s. The self-portrait pictured here was done when she was 80 years old. The painting is widely regarded as a bold statement against an ageist and sexist society. By portraying herself without any clothes while confidently holding a paintbrush, Neel defied the societal norms that dictated how women should present themselves.

A Woman's Body, Remembering
Jan Seale

A hot coin spoke from one side,
a dog of a backache sniped.
The legs were pillars of Samson,
and the head, a swarm of gnats.
Why then, do I miss you,
Aunt Flo, Little Visitor,
Ragtime Sally, Queen's X,
you who have taken yourself away,
tightlipped, silent?

Sometimes I lie in bed calling to you
from the second half of my life.
Remember me?
Remember my useful body?
You came to me, made me
a worker of the world each month,
told me—you comforting clock,
scenic calendar page,
baby maker/trouble maker,
cascade of moon juice,
Rorschach quilt—
that I was all right.

If I could,
I would curl into you for five days,
go sit in my little hut,
without men, without kitchen duty,
curl nights into you,
be an embryo of the moon;

I would begin with ocher clay,
move on to the true flush of poppies,
and finally, would-be baby pink,
all these colors in health—
on a canvas of winning landscape;
this would be folded in linen,
handled only with clean hands,
laid in a cedar trunk,
brought out on feast days
to show my daughters-in-law:
"This is the original stuff of your husband.
Now go and paint your own."

Today, my body remote as an elevated railway,
like soap, like the horizon,
my body wishes to remember.

God's bound to be a woman sometimes,
to think up this bright paint between the legs.
Where else is flowing blood the picture of health,
a lovely joke about the future?

PUBIC ENEMY
SUSAN TERRIS

Shave it, wax it, pluck the black coils
Escaping your bikini bottom.

Brazilian, French—the triangle, sphynx,
The landing strip, moustache, the heart.

A source of obsession. But older now,
Much much older....

Where is that burning bush?

HYGIENE
ALICE FRIMAN

When Miss Garvey preached
about the importance of washing
beneath our breasts, we were barely
fourteen. We of the pert and perky,
the new sproutings of last spring.
We of the rose-tipped sundae.
We of the smart-aleck mouth:
what's this "beneath" business?
There was no beneath. We were up-
standing in duplicate and up to date—
saucy, sassy, and more relevant
than we knew. We were upright,
up-and-coming, immortal as summer,
flushed as the cherry in our cheeks.

The only beneath that counted
was beneath a sweater, pointing
to the endless possibilities of
where we thought we were headed.
When we stood firm in our straps,
weren't we, for the first time, armed
with power? The lure of I-dare-you
under the do-not-touch of delicious?

To Miss Garvey—object of our
ninth-grade derision—I apologize,
for now, now that I've gotten so old,
I have indeed developed an under,
a beneath. Sometimes I hear
her muffled voice lecturing from
my own dark crease where she lives,
hunkered down, grousing like

the troll under the bridge and wagging
her finger in perpetual admonition—
hygiene, hygiene. Oh for the days
before underwire and under performance,
each morning cup tilted fresh and sweet.

LETTER TO GOD, WHOMEVER
RHODA MAE EVANS

—apologies to Samuel Beckett,
the missing mouse,
and lung.

yank my arm off—okey
but not my breasts yet.
you already failed at that.
take my toes, fungus and all.
they served me well—walked
across the country, danced
four days a week, no blisters ever.
they may serve you well as well.
take my hip (s) they could shimmy,
sashay at (in) appropriate times.
take my grotesque fingers, gnarling
up for years, no rings fit anymore
but they can still juggle. you already
have my uterus but I'm grateful you
waited, left me time to use it. okey,
you killed one baby but gave me two
others of the perfect human kind.
forage my gall bladder and spleen,
I hardly know they're there.
you got my tonsils when I was sixteen,
the same year you took my hymen,
you took my appendix at sixty.
what is it with you and inner body parts?
are they a delicacy, served up for a feast?
why the hell do you leave hemorrhoids,
not tasty enough for you? or do you just

find pain and humiliation hilarious?
they are funny, like hitting the funny bone.
take what we used to call private parts
I don't use them anymore, but you can
leave the G-spot until all is shriveled.
it's still useful until I'm G one. you will not
be forgiven if you do. just give me back the
little mouse, with the huge grey ears,
who sat on my shoulder when I was a child
and protected me, now, as imaginary as you.
I believe you are one odd G od oh
amen, awomen, athey........
Auto-da-Fe

AS THEY SAY, HIP, HIP, HOORAY
ROSANNE EHRLICH

Hip Replacement, Hip Replace Hip, Replacement, Hip Replace Hip, Replacement of Hip, Replace Hip, Replacement, Hip replacement. Three weeks, 21 days, till the Hip Replacement.

Let's see, 19 days away from um, ah, the hip...operation and the first thing I do is call Westmed and piss off the doctor's assistant, Maggie, by careless use of humor when I was asked, if I were ready, if I had any questions, I asked if *they* were ready. Boy did I get off on the wrong foot. Oy. I dared to disturb the universe.

Day 13: Different acquaintances, who still have all their original parts, tell me, "I had three friends who had them, and their lives are changed. It was really no big deal." "You'll be so happy you did it." "You'll lose some weight." Then there's "What hospital are you going to? Who's your doctor?" I resist answering: "In the Irvington town garage, they're sweeping the floor." Only once did I slip and say this to Marty, my 70-year-old accountant, who then told me he went to the best hospital where the head orthopedic surgeon replaced his and the finest plastic surgeon in the city closed his wound. "I have no scars," he said. He was doing my taxes, so I nodded appreciatively.

A little more than a week to go. As my mother used say, "It's your own fault." Three days and one week to go. I couldn't resist the on-line "Hip Replacement Support" groups. Today, exactly ten and a half days before...while trying to not look at them on-line I came across one on Facebook. Why did I sign up? I thought it was a good idea at the time to just put off mentioning what I soon read on-line. *"Woman goes in for Hip Replacement Surgery, comes out of it in a coma and later dies."* It could have been the tiny print of the Internet, but I saw it as a dark black *New York Post* headline.

Day 10: *"Infected hip, drainage infected."* The next day, I was just looking to see what a friend who was on a book tour is doing, another friend was hiking Machu Pichu, somebody else was biking in a marathon, and dancing the tango with her grandson on a cruise. Well, I'm having an adventure too, I try to think. *"I had hip replacement 8 months* ago but when I bend down the pain is severe in my leg where the bone hits the metal." Titanium, I remember, I'm not allergic to that. That's a good thing. Remember that.

A few days later: The perils of too much preparation, thought the woman who has not been doing the required exercising. Is this really happening? Back to the internet. Watch out for the focus group. Just peek at it for a few quick horror stories and pleas to end the pain... well, not that bad. "Having some severe swelling from my hip to my foot." I tell myself that my way of dealing with it is to try not to think about it too much.

Next day: Back to business. I should focus on the details of being out of commission for a few days. Looking at Amazon for all those tools, I read all about sock pull-ups, long distance pincers if something is on the floor, sling to lift your leg up onto the bed, breathing thing so you don't get pneumonia. Don't look at all those entries, I tell myself.

"I just want the pain to go away." "Will I be able to wipe myself?" Ooops, I slipped but read on as follows: "My friend died here last week from this surgery." I squint when I go over all the selfies, it's like a black and white photo of the Battlefield at Gettysburg....Littered with bad news. "I'm 6 weeks post-op and I feel like I'm getting worse instead of better. Has anyone been left with permanent nerve damage or muscle damage? I'm so depressed."

Five days to go, just before the hip replacement operation which I'm trying not to think about too much, I go to TJ MAXX where everybody looks like me but a little more fashionably dressed and not limping. I get a gray jersey shift with little pink hearts, it's soft. I try it on at home and look like my worst self. Thirteen years old again.

Next day and only four days to go. I drive back (will I be able to drive if it's "only my left hip"?) to a different TJ MAXX with the same Westchester clientele to return the first one and get another nightgown which turns out to be too short, totally wrong.

Three more days to Operation Day: What will happen in the operating room? How will that go, how will I be? I enjoy being put out, but then I remember, again, the woman who came out of her hip replacement surgery in a coma and later died, which the support site helpfully posted. Tomorrow I see the surgeon. Is he *"the best"?* Everybody else has gone to "the best." Maggie, his assistant, will be there, maybe bringing her some candy will help. I think of other hospital stays, hernia operation, childbirth, not the worst as long as they put you out. Well, maybe childbirth is the worst.

Day two, back at TJ MAXX after deciding the second nightgown wasn't right. To think, at my age, this is going on. I could be dead, I am well aware. Not yet, but I did reply to the doctor's question about my mental state of health. "Any questions about the procedure?" "Other than, will I die on the operating table?" He laughed.

Day before: I go swimming for the last time. Then into the neighborhood hardware store and a cute older gentleman with a slight accent seems very interested in helping me and making general conversation. I make a joke about my coming hip replacement, and he says both his hips have been replaced. "Best thing I ever did," he says.

Rubber hits the road kind of thing…tomorrow morning. Still 12 hours away, my stomach lurches as I think this. It's almost over, it occurs to me. You could go at any minute. Or get this hip replaced and snap out of it, already. Boy, do I ache. Very little stamina. Maybe this hip operation could be a good thing.

Operation Day: I look at the fluorescent lights on the hallway ceiling as I'm being wheeled to the operating room. Will I make it? The operating room is full of people.…

- - - -

I wake but doze through the day. In the evening they get me up to walk and I have no pain. I feel like I'm being warmed by the sun. What would I wear in Machu Pichu?

NOTHING CAN SAVE US
ROSIE KING

What then
shall we do
loving the sun
that yo-yo swirl of yellow
we drew in our
cornflower skies

counted on to flirt
among the curly white clouds
above the elms
to make fragrant even the dust
we spun up from
the cracks in the sidewalk

sun
that warmed us
freckled our skin
and that we learn
only slowly
one day won't miss us a bit

Nothing can stop them
says my young nephew
pointing to the wrinkles
on my outstretched arm
not even
being content

WHAT MIGHT HAPPEN
ROSIE KING

Gingersnap, coconut, slivered almonds
struck together with a glaze
surely sugar—

yet with tea, chamomile so calming
who knows what tip
of an insight

might rise
unbidden, uncoaxed, unbound
to pierce the day—

a snowcap
I'd get up and dress for, some
meeting out there with a

spruce on the road
or a face with fresh eyes, yours
maybe, and a voice

to sweeten
and steady me
for the steep uphill

NOW THAT I'M ALMOST PERFECT
FLORENCE WEINBERGER

I began to notice it years ago, when
Trader Joe's spicy spaghetti sauce,
balanced flavors, just the right tang,
suddenly vanished, never to reappear.
I could list dozens of products that
fit like a glove, sneakers, for instance,
I once found and loved and tried to
reorder, and you guessed it, they're
gone. Like forever, though sometimes
you find a leftover pair in a warehouse
somewhere or stuck behind a fake
Tiffany lamp in an outlet store.

                Of course they do it
on purpose, some marketing ploy
I never got. Then there's the perfect
day that ends, the faultless friend
who betrays, the lover who dies.
You can see it's a trend. I know,
I'm straying from my rant against
blatant commercialism; I'll end up
exhorting the gods, *what are you*
selling? Why would you stamp me
with such a short shelf life, a just-
around-the-corner expiration date,
when I'm on the verge of getting
flavored with just the right tang?

Who's Perfect?
Carol McMahon

Adonis was waiting by the reception desk in the sleek fitness studio on the edge of Munich's Englischer Garten. Wise of him. Anyone else on his staff of young, lithe, sculpted bodies would have told me I was in the wrong place. A personal trainer at my age? Was thinking I could get in shape, be fit like Jane Fonda, the beginning of senility? Her appearance in the DVD workout she'd made at age seventy had motivated me to get off my duff and go for the "burn" again. Of course, everything Jane did, she did perfectly. My mantra was G. K. Chesterton's aphorism: *Anything worth doing is worth doing badly.*

"Let's first go to my office. You can tell me what you want in privacy."
Kind of him.

During the six weeks I'd had to wait for an appointment, I had done exercises to strengthen the teres minor muscle to prevent buffalo's hump. I'd done balancing exercises and stretched my hamstrings. I took Jane's advice and engaged stomach muscles whether I was sitting, standing, or walking. Just as I cleaned the house before any cleaning help came, I had felt compelled to train before seeing a personal trainer.

"Forget doing one thousand reps in different directions to strengthen little accessory muscles. I'm not trying to look like Shakira. I want someone to assess my body's vulnerabilities, give me some exercises to maintain what an eighty-year-old can, and goad me."

"Okay, but to start any exercise program, you'll need to get approval from a medical doctor."

"I used to jog and ride a bicycle. Now I walk a lot."

"Good, but you'll still need to have a medical checkup. For instance, if you have osteoporosis, hi-impact is out; moving certain ways may cause bone fractures and spine crushes."

"How about starting me off with exercises that are safe for all senior citizens?"

"Have you thought about going to a German *Krankengymnastin?*"
"That isn't what I had in mind."
"Your health insurance would pay."

"I'm familiar with the benefits of German health insurance."

"You'll work with a medically trained person."

"I'd be more motivated by something less like rehab."

"They monitor your progress."

"I'd be cheered by something less clinical, more aesthetic. It's the same with body creams. I use them when they come in pretty bottles."

"That makes the price higher without any more guarantees."

"At my age, there are no guarantees. I'll sign a liability waver."

His eyes shifted left. "Look, we want you to attain your goal, but we personal trainers also want to feel good about what we do."

Was he saying personal trainers wouldn't feel good helping an octogenarian get in shape? "Would you be willing to start me off with some simple exercises that would get me fit enough for fitness training later?"

"Yes—after you've seen a doctor. Just scan the approval and email it to us, then call for another appointment."

"Can I make another appointment now with you?"

"I'd rather wait until you've been to the doctor."

"Having another appointment will make sure I go."

He sighed and checked his appointment sheet. "How about six weeks from now, Tuesday, same time?"

"I'll take it."

He started for the door.

"Can't you show me something useful that I could be doing during those six weeks?"

He looked at his watch, then reached for a notepad. "Here's a website with some great exercises for strength and balance building. Just follow the instructions online and you can't do any harm."

Wasn't it just like the younger generation to resort to the digital world? And that "just scan it," as though everybody had a way to scan! If getting fit meant going to cyberspace, I could make myself do that even though I loathed spending time recalling passwords, updating programs, finding sites, and attaching documents on my computer.

Another six weeks? I could die before then. Maybe that's what the Adonis was counting on. To his credit, the website he'd referred me to was a government site for senior citizens, full of useful information. The section on exercise was excellent, written in large print accompanied by good animations to demonstrate the correct movements. Maintenance was already taking up a good bit of my day, but I could see the wisdom of incorporating several of the demonstrated exercises in my daily routine.

Getting that required doctor's approval, however, hovered on the horizon. I dithered. I delayed. Why did I procrastinate? Since my wonderful German general practitioner had retired and taken her eye contact and old-fashioned bedside manners with her, I'd experienced nothing in doctor's offices but baby-faced technicians. They stared at their digital devices during the fifteen minutes allotted to me, typing in my answers to their short questions. If a question from me deviated from their flow chart, they were silent or answered, "That's not my specialty."

There had been a few exceptions. One doctor, after glancing at the birthdate in my records when I said I'd had a dizzy spell, did face me and asked what I expected at my age. A skin doctor had summoned her medical colleagues, who scrutinized me while I stood naked and shivering in her examining room. "We don't get to see something like this often," she had said. One young economically-minded gynecologist had his examining table placed so that my private parts got the light from the floor to ceiling windows. Probing my insides on a sunny day, he looked through my spread legs and smiled to reassure me—so did the office workers in the building across the courtyard. But, in addition, they waved.

I concluded the main reason I hesitated going to the doctor was because of the problems I'd had getting health insurance. After the death of my husband, I was shocked to learn that I, his spouse, no longer was covered by our American health policy. I approached several German insurance companies, but, as soon as they discovered my age and that I resided in Germany, they hustled me out the door. They wouldn't return my calls when I left a message. Consequently, I went to a doctor only for emergencies. A medical checkup for a private trainer? Couldn't justify the hassle.

Having performed the recommended exercises on the government site for a couple of weeks, I was ready for a little more pizazz. While googling for "workouts," I happened upon a flamenco demonstration video on YouTube. The more mature the women dancers were, the better they danced—and they needed no partner. Flamenco seemed perfect for me. I ordered a couple of instructional DVDs and bought a ruffled flamenco skirt. Practicing the foot work, the skirt swishing, and the hand movements in the privacy of my apartment was exhilarating. I became hooked on flamenco and forgot about doctors.

My stamina increased, my posture improved, my arms started to have some definition, and my feet no longer felt like stiff boards. I felt so good it dawned on me that I didn't need a personal trainer. To celebrate, I threw away all my dingy-looking underwear and bought new undergarments—cheery ones that made my clothesline look like a string of colored Christmas lights on laundry days. Did I dare buy those flamenco shoes with heels full of iron nails?

The second time I practiced stamping with my new *zapatos flamencos*, the doorbell rang. I ignored it. The ringing persisted. With a red rose stuck in my grey hair, wearing my flamenco skirt and a tank top, I went to the door. It was the occupant of the apartment below mine.

"I'm sorry to have to complain, but I can't concentrate on my work with all that hammering."

"I'm sorry, as well."

"When will the workers be finished?"

"I'll stop now."

He looked confused. Rather than leaving, he took in my outfit.

"Are you Spanish?"

"No. I'm learning to dance flamenco."

He froze, mouth half-open, staring at me. I thought I'd make extrication easy for him by bidding goodbye and shutting the door.

"Wait! Flamenco dancing sounds interesting."

"It is. I'll be quiet now. *Auf Wiedersehen.*"

He thrust his foot forward.

"Would you show me?"

"I'm not good enough to give a demonstration."

"Even a bad performance would interest me."

"I'm just beginning."

"Do you enjoy it?"

"Oh, yes!"

"Then that's the main thing. May I at least see what you use for instructions?"

"It's just a DVD… but, yes, of course. Come in."

Somehow he got me to dance. He thought I was great.

"That guitar music is passionate."

"Yes, it is."

"Do men dance the flamenco?"

"I believe they do."

"It seems an excellent way to stay in shape."

"That's why I started it."

He seemed so interested that I found myself explaining how it all had begun, how I had tried to hire a personal trainer, but had balked at getting the required medical approval because I didn't want to pay for a medical examination.

"But German health insurance would cover that."

"I know, but to me personal training doesn't really qualify for reimbursement."

"But all the Germans go to gymnastics and use their insurance to pay."

"That doesn't seem moral. Besides, I don't have German health insurance."

"You don't have German health insurance?"

"No, I couldn't get accepted by a company."

Furrows appeared between his eyebrows. Bright red spots bloomed on his cheeks. "Excuse me, I should have introduced myself sooner. Stamitz. Klaus Stamitz. I work for a health insurance company."

I felt embarrassment, then dread. Would I now get into trouble with the German authorities? Somehow wearing a flamenco skirt and a rose in my hair gave me courage. I stood straight and held out my hand. "Sib. Sib Stalwart. I wish I'd met you earlier."

He reddened. "Everyone has a right to health care. Besides, you must have it; it's a law in Germany."

Herr Stamitz delineated the problems I'd have if I didn't possess that little piece of plastic indicating that I was "in the system." Rather than stating I knew that from firsthand experience, I offered him a glass of wine. By the time we finished the bottle, he had explained all the benefits of the system and promised to see if there wasn't some way he could get me coverage with his company.

The next day I found forms in the mailbox and a note to fill them out and return them to him. The note was signed "Klaus" which seemed like progress in getting to know at least one of my German neighbors. What did I have to lose except the few minutes it took to answer all the questions? Those proved hard to find because what had promised to be an open, calm day wasn't.

The telephone rang.

"Sib here."

"Sib, is that really you?" a woman's voice asked. "This is Marie."

"Marie! Are you in Munich?"

"I'm calling from Italy."

"Italy? Quick, give me your number! We'll get disconnected."

I heard Marie's tinkly laugh. "I'll call back."

"Where exactly are you?"

"Rome."

"What are you doing there?"

"It's a long story. What are you doing in Munich?"

"It's a long story."

"Can we get together?"

"You want to come to Germany?"

"No! You want to come to Italy?"

"Yes!"

"I have some connections and can get you into the Vatican after hours. If you don't mind sleeping under a crucifix, I can find accommodations for you in a convent."

"When can I come?"

"Tomorrow!"

Agreeing to talk again after I'd made travel arrangements, I was eager to hang up and start packing, but Marie wasn't finished.

"Make sure your German health insurance will cover you here."

I took a deep breath and explained my problems with getting health coverage.

"Get a lawyer! Everyone I know who lives in Germany has to have one."

That seemed a bit much to me, and I dismissed her words as Italian theatrics. When I sat down at the desk to make a list of things I needed to arrange, I found Klaus's insurance application forms. Feeling that long shot could wait, I pushed them aside. Had Klaus not rung the doorbell, I'd probably have forgotten them.

"It's good you dropped by. I'll be away for a couple of weeks. It'll be quiet for you."

"It'll take some time to process the forms anyway. Do you have them filled out?"

"I'm sorry, no."

"I'll wait."

"Look, you've been more than kind, but I don't have much confidence about this, and I'm reluctant to pass myself off as something I'm not."

He cast a pitiful look at me. "You don't know how things work in Germany, do you?"

"Maybe not, but I don't have a sense of entitlement."

"There are just a few questions. Please answer them."

"Why is this so important for you?"

"I told you I believe everyone deserves health coverage." When that didn't convince me, he added, "I promised my mother I'd help you."

"Huh?"

His face showed a struggle taking place inside. He pointed to my front window. "See those lace curtains across the street? My mother lies behind them, bedridden. We have her bed pushed up to the window. She can see into your apartment, sort of uses it as her reality TV. She's a devoted fan of yours."

Speechless, I stared out the window. I thought I saw a hand wave. "Why does she want to help me?"

"You're an American." A trace of a smile passed over his lips. "She's fascinated by your lifestyle."

I must have looked skeptical because he continued his explanation: "The Americans saved her and her sister when they marched into Munich. Without the help of the G.I.'s, they wouldn't have made it, and I wouldn't be here."

"I'm touched. Thank her."

I motioned for him to sit down, inserted a flamenco guitar music

CD in the player and pointed to the earphones. I picked up the questionnaire, filled it out, and handed it to him just as he was starting to stamp his feet.

He reoriented, went to the window, and waved the papers. Then, he left.

I went back to making a list of things to do for my trip to Italy, still thinking about Frau Stamitz across the street. She and I were two old women. What was better? Dying in one's own apartment or somewhere else? In a hotel room, someone would find me sooner. In another country, strangers would, without fuss or remorse, do what needed to be done. Costs would be taken care of if I purchased travel insurance. It dawned on me that taking trips might be the solution to both my health care problem and my determination to die enjoying myself. It wasn't perfect, but what was?

Post Cataract Surgery
Perie Longo

Blur gone, eyes zapped with lens implants,
the world suddenly boggles, too brilliant.
Greens of Spring stun with pixilated glimmer.

Fuchsia Bougainvillea boogies over walls,
golden designs on the lizard's back amaze and I'm shocked
to see some tree topping La Cumbre peak

leaning against the blue blast of sky. Unfortunately,
the mountain's crevices and creases duplicate
newly emerged canyons in my face, once mere wrinkles

I complain to a friend after her same procedure.
And those pores, she cries in horror. We grit our teeth,
leaving the matter of bridges alone. Especially crossing

dark waters of the unknown in tandem,
moaning *we are not aliens* staring back at ourselves
from the lit mirror, eyes dripping gooey drops.

I did not ask for this kind of clarity,
only wanted to rid haloes from street lights
driving home after dark and arrive intact, yet still

they throb like strung-out angels. By day, I live
under cover wearing new Ray-Bans.

Blur is better our age, God's idea of peace,
reward for long life in an overwhelming world.

Can I have my cataracts back? I ask my doctor.
He stares sharply. Delivers
the name of a psychiatrist on a yellow sticky note
and a prescription for sleep.

FALL RISK
PERIE LONGO

Soon after hip surgery repair,
ball in socket kind of thing, 2:00 am,
I try to turn. An alarm shrieks.
The night nurse rushes into my room.
"You can't move," she says,
"you'll wake the dead." I thought I was.

A red plastic bracelet tells the story: FALL RISK,
also written on the wall chart above my bed.
Not even my name. Is this what I'm reduced to?
Why do I keep throwing myself to the ground,
three times this year alone, as if
in supplication saying *sorry, sorry.*

Not on purpose, mind you. I once read
when our woes get the best of us, kneel down
on Earth and breathe troubles into her arms.
She'll manage everything. I was young then,
always one with patchwork clouds
tinted gold, and hawks holding court treetop
at dusk. Now look at me, a Fall Risk
imprisoned in rehab and Earth choked in all the ways
we've reduced her to parch. It seems strange

to tell you this but when I found myself
immobile in pain on the asphalt, I figured
a gremlin's hand had reached up to punish me for
some unknown transgression. I was alone,
feebly calling *help. Please help.* No response,

yet there was a fleeting moment
I felt part of so many others around the world,
all of us falling one way or another
connected beyond anything that makes sense.

I breathed out and somehow came to be
on the other side of the sirens, raising the ire
of the night nurse. As she wheels me
to the rest room, I tell her I have a whole list
of other more interesting risks, if she's up for it.
In the backlight, she bursts out laughing
our revelry real as any prayer.

BEING SENIOR
PERIE LONGO

Takes a village to finish your sentence,
the condition sentence enough, word sought
jammed between dream and next sip of dark roast.

Put downs come to mind.
"Carry out, ma'am?" Not there yet.
"You still here?" Last time I looked!

So many questions at our age.
"Just worn cartilage," the orthopedist tosses off,
lighting up my knee x-ray. "What's next?" I ask.
"Nothing," he says.

Last night in the parking lot after the theater,
my friend can't find her car. "It's new, all electric,
gray." She click-clicks her key thing.
I drive her up and down the aisles of cars,

all unresponsive shadows in night's gloom,
no little red lights blinking "here."
"Oh," she remembers with a lurch,
"I parked it on the street."

Another friend, only weeks ago, his children weeping
bedside, rose from a near coma.
"Laugh!" he ordered with vigor and sank
without ceremony. *Dropped away like a petal,*

his last word etched in memory
as winter wind releases a blizzard of white
from the flowering pear tree, filling every speck of air,
every cranny, every niche, nothing left to say.

WHISKEY AND HOT WATER
PATRICIA HUKILL

Yesterday, I sat, wrapped in my heavy
fleece pink robe, heating pad over
neuropathic toes, staring happily ahead.
We know bears do it.
Give up in winter, give in to the closing
down all around, as the maples shut down
in a blaze of color. Succulents cuddling
together in their circle of support.
Only the trail walkers persist,
the old ones outside my window, trudging,
limping, dragging their dogs behind them,
instructed by their doctor…don't let up.
Old Age will catch you in a week.

Today, Old Age, I welcome you. Come catch me.
Be my companion, today. I will fetch you a blanket,
a cup of hot whiskey and water. We will sit together
for a time and recognize each other.

WHAT A RELIEF
PATRICIA HUKILL

after all those years
of restraint, your mind
filtering diligently
before you speak
so that what you say
is appropriate and nuanced
and suitable for the occasion
scientists now learn that
a lobe of the brain
starts shrinking
at a certain age,
the part that censors,
so that whatever
comes out of your mouth
will be a surprise
to other people
and yourself.
You cringe at a party,
hearing an opinion
loosely thrown about,
rather rudely,
and it's yours.
Can't you just see
all those pent-up words
pushing at the faulty gate,
insisting that,
by the end
all of their voices
be heard.

ABOUT BEING OLD
WENDY TAYLOR CARLISLE

I don't often write about being old, but
the former century is at the bottom of every day,
the residue in the teapot,

the cobweb I didn't see when I was on the ladder,
armadillo in the garden, scything away
at the pepper plants. It's not as if I don't remember

my sons' formula breath or holding my grandsons
hostage on my lap but I've been wary,
of child-gossip and nursery-confession.

More often I write sex and loss, the one
mostly over, the other hissing out slowly
like a gas leak. Don't misunderstand—

not love songs about the damned moon
but hard breath and sweat, and mean shoes,
oh, and drinking, shutting the bar down.

Still, aspiration and curiosity remain, the donkey work
of lyric, meanwhile swiping the cobweb,
swallowing the leaves stuck at the bottom of the cup.

SECOND WAVE
WENDY TAYLOR CARLISLE

Here we are, the girls who bonded
reading *Our Bodies, Ourselves,*
who checked our vaginas in hand mirrors
and were surprised,
who were taught by our mothers to be wary of
girlfriends, our enemies in the war
for men and territory, taught
that desire was man's privilege and
that joy was impossible without his embrace.
Now, on the other side of hormones, we see
our mothers lied like presidents.

FALLING DOWN
IRENE SARDANIS

If you've missed seeing me and wonder where I've been for the last year, I can tell you now. I've been hiding. It's taken all this time to come out of hibernation. Now I think I'm ready to share what happened.

The thrift store at the lake is one I've been to many times. My immigrant mother taught me well to always go for the bargains. She would haggle with the produce sellers for the ripe tomatoes and ask them to throw in a green pepper, too. I was ashamed of her doing that, reminding me we were poor with little money for anything after the rent was paid. She was a peasant from a small village in Greece. As the youngest, I was held hostage by her needs, which were many. I was her go-for, the errand girl, the translator since she spoke no English. When I misbehaved, lied, or defied her, she would send those Greek curses at me which I believed had the power to destroy me. Her influence had stayed with me long after her death.

With my old sweats threadbare, I looked in the aisles in the thrift store for the ones that might be my size, then looked for fitting rooms to try them on.

"No fitting rooms," the woman at the counter said. "After Covid-19, we had to close them."

I took the pants and with nothing to hang on to, tried to put them on, standing up, but I tripped over to my right and with no support, fell over. I went down and in slow motion I saw myself going over and hitting the floor hard. I tried to get up, but the pain in my hip was at a level ten. A woman came over and tried to lift me. I screamed.

At the hospital, they took x-rays and surgery was scheduled for the following day. I wanted to be free of pain and just get the procedure over with. Little did I know that procedure was a two and a half hour surgery to mend my broken hip.

The familiar guilt/blame/shame at the whole catastrophe after the fall, hit me.

GUILT. I did it. I'm to blame, and I deserve to be punished. Stupid, dumb bitch. I was responsible for this accident. I was not paying attention.

Why didn't I sit on the floor to try them on? I thought I could balance myself, standing on one foot, yoga style. Yeah, sure.

BLAME. Yes, I was to blame for not being careful and falling, but what about the store's responsibility? Why the hell didn't they provide support for someone like me, a senior? It was their fault that I fell.

Then the familiar question came to me as to whether my mother was still cursing me from her grave. If you're ethnic as in Chinese, Mexican, Iranian, Indian or any culture that includes the evil eye, you'll understand why I felt my mother's ghost was alive and haunting my life.

SHAME. Why did I even go into that thrift store for sweatpants when I could well afford to pay full price at any upscale store like Macy's or even Saks Fifth Avenue? Why at this stage of my life am I still attached to my mother's life of poverty? Oh, great shame!

PHASE ONE: THE HOSPITAL

I was given a room of my own. Tubes were hooked to my arm. I felt like a zombie, a robot with someone else in control of my body. Time as I knew it no longer existed. The day, the time, the date. None of it held any interest for me anymore. I was in a time warp.

Depression. I had no conscious plan to end my life, yet some part of me that I didn't want to admit to, gave up on living. What the hell for? I saw nothing in the future that held any promise for me. All I could see was me, an old, decrepit cripple who no one would want in their life, certainly not my vibrant, gorgeous energetic husband.

It was like the old me had died and I needed to grieve her demise. I didn't know who I was anymore or what I'd look like when this was all over. It reminded me of a time when I could drive and saw a bumper sticker with the words—Caution, the driver of this car just doesn't give a damn. Yes, I could identify. Me too.

PHASE TWO: RECOVERY

My husband was eager to have me home again, but that wasn't going to happen as soon as he wanted. There was more rehab, a place where physiotherapists would begin the process of teaching me how to walk again. I was given a walker to help me get back on my feet. With no desire to use it, I ignored the urges from staff to try it. I just wanted to stay in bed.

Each day at the rehab center the physiotherapist got me out of bed to practice using the walker until I could walk the halls in the facility, slowly, without her assistance. After a week, I was discharged to go home, but I was afraid to leave. How would I even get into my house?

PHASE THREE: GOING HOME

John was over the top with joy to have me home again. To prepare for my arrival, he single-handedly moved our queen-sized bed closer to the toilet so I would not have to walk far to use it, especially at night. The bed weighed a ton. How the hell did he do that without any help?

Friends called, eager to visit, wanting to help in any way. They missed me, they said. I put them off. Not yet, I said. I'm not ready to see anyone. I'm not worth a visit.

When my legs felt strong enough to walk outside the house, I became a passenger in John's car. Would I ever get to drive my own car again, I wondered? It had been four months since I drove. After a visit with my doctor, he reassured me I'd drive again soon. He gave me hope.

THE STAIR ELEVATOR

We talked about it. I struggled against getting one. Maybe we could wait until I could walk up and down the fifteen steps to the garage the way I used to. Not a reality.

Finally, to hell with the expense, John said. We're installing the stair lift. It covered the fifteen steps to the house from the garage, giving me access to my car. I wept with gratitude when the installer completed the job and showed me how to use it.

THE THREE FALLS

The first one was at the bathroom sink. One minute I was washing my hands, the next one was me on the floor with no idea how I got there. John was nearby to pick me up. How did this happen? And there she was again, my mother. Was her evil spirit still around to curse me? The second one a few weeks later was at John's car after a Chinese dinner. The third one was at our garage as I walked towards John's car. I tripped again on uneven ground and landed on my right side. This fall scared me. My right side was where I'd had surgery to repair the hip. Had I broken anything? Did I need an x-ray? I called my doctor who asked if I could walk. Yes. Was I in pain? No. She said inside the house use the cane. Outside, use the walker. Okay, I got it.

My hair had grown. When I looked in the mirror, I saw an old straggly-haired woman. I needed a haircut badly. I found a salon in a shopping center nearby. As the beautician cut my hair, a new face emerged from the mirror.

Sex. Being intimate with John no longer held any interest for me. After a zoom meeting with my therapist, she reminded me my body was still healing. She encouraged me to just touch and kiss him. Go slow, she said. That, I thought I could do.

After breakfast one morning John surprised me. Hey, he said, why don't we go to Hawaii after Christmas? Oh no, no, I thought. What are you saying? It's too soon, way too soon for me to travel. I didn't know whether I could make it to downtown Berkeley, let alone get on a plane to Hawaii. Despite my reservations, I knew this trip to Hawaii was important. Not for me. It was for John. He deserved a vacation from all the caretaking he did for me.

There was not much to do in Hawaii but breathe in that tropical air, rest, relax, read books, savor the sunsets. Oh, and heal.

Home, I faced my mother's fears again. There she was sitting on my doorstep, waiting to belittle me, crush me down. Yet after this trip, I felt changed. Something inside had shifted.

"Ma," I said facing her. "You can't come into my house anymore. It's time for you to leave. Now."

Usually, I'd ask my mother for forgiveness, for not being the daughter she wanted, for rebelling and defying her. But now, I did not wither up and go into some corner and crumble. For some reason I could not fathom, I felt worthy of my life without the usual guilt and pain.

This time I looked her square in the face and said: You need to stop. *Stamata,* I said. You must leave now and get the hell out of my psyche and brain. I'm tired of your threats and curses. I believed I deserved your cruelty, that I was a terrible kid. Enough. I'm going to do battle with you every time you try to destroy me.

For once, she has no response. She gets it but doesn't like it one bit. She gets that I'm through with her control over my life, her unexpected surprises. We sit in silence. I rise and open the door to my home. I look at her crumbled old body, shaking her head in disbelief. I close the door and enter my welcoming home. Enough already. I'm not sure how much time I've got left of this life, but whatever it is, I'm planning to move, to walk, run and dance again. It's time to enjoy the rest of my life.

Opa. Let's dance.

A DIGRESSION ON HEALTH CARE
MARGE PIERCY

In some ways, being old is like being poor in the quality of health care you usually receive. And if you are poor, middle class and professional people assume you're stupid. When you're poor and when you're elderly, you are spoken to as if you were semi-idiotic. It seems to be assumed you won't understand medical terms and everything has to be put in simple phrases, you, poor dear, can comprehend.

When I was a child, a doctor was called to the house once for me. I had the German Measles and then Rheumatic Fever—the doctor came, diagnosed me for five minutes and said I'd be dead in a week, $10 cash please.

When I was seventeen, I took myself to a dentist near the phone company where I was working a split shift. He looked in my mouth, said I had three bad cavities. He asked me how much money I had. I told him. He said, that's not enough for fillings. I'll pull them. And he did. Public health in the States is a bad joke.

When I was in England before going to France with the man who'd be my first husband, I was shocked by the doctors I saw. I couldn't get birth control in the States since I wasn't married. In England, under socialized medicine, the doctor said, Of course you want birth control, and fitted me with what they called a pessary. The physical exam was thorough as was the level of attention.

I had reasonably good and sometimes excellent health care once I started to make money off my writing and appearances. Health care in the Outer Cape was of high quality for many decades but now there are serious problems. Few doctors, nurses, medical personnel can afford the ridiculously inflated houses that wealthy people and their real estate agents have created.

I keep returning to my recent history. We learned I had all the classic symptoms of heart failure. I can't understand how both doctors I saw missed it all. It wasn't as if I didn't mention that my blood pressure that had always been quite low was slowly climbing, that my ankles and feet were swollen, that I was gaining weight, that I could do little exercise without running out of energy, that I experienced shortness of breath upon ordinary activities like climbing stairs. I'd always had a strong heart, but at 86, you'd think they'd notice. Women don't get the heart attention that men do.

I sometimes wonder if I should have died and if I'm somehow inappropriately stealing this time.

Part Seven

CIRCLE OF LIFE

The path is not long but the way is deep.
You must not only walk there, but be prepared to leap.
—St. Hildegard of Bingen, 1098-1179
German Benedictine Abbess,
writer, mystic, and medical practitioner.

On the fields of Kasuga
Piled snow is all
I see, yet
Sprouting up
Are fresh shoots.

—Akazome Emon, 956-1041
Honored Japanese court poet.

Dawn comes slowly but dusk is rapid.
—Alice B. Toklas, 1877-1967
Cookbook author and
member of the Parisian avant-garde.

I said to the Lord, I'm going to hold steady on to you, and I know you will
see me through.
—Harriet Tubman, 1822-1913
American abolitionist and
Underground Railroad freedom fighter.

I am haunted by ghosts of so many writers, characters from my stories, of
people whom I have "lived" and yes loved and lost. Sometimes I feel like an
old house that is privy to simultaneous conversations of its inhabitants.
Not always a privilege!
—Mahasweta Devi, 1926-2016
Bengali poet and activist.

MEDITATION
MARILYN ROBERTSON

Animals cross the field, collecting night.
The dark eyes of solitude look my way.

I stand where you stood,
I with my one dream, you with your two.

Once there were ten chores done before sunrise.
Now a pile of books brings in the dawn.

Bodies change shape, faces become maps
Even the experienced traveler must read again.

Our bones begin to long for earth,
Star returning to star, dreaming its original light.

Everything flows toward love...
The small river, the bigger one to come.

Bar Codes
Bonnie Wehle

Neil Armstrong had just landed on the moon.
The country was filled with space-shot fervor;
I wore tinfoil antennae
to a dress as-in-the-future costume party,
drew bar codes on my wrists,
which I imagined when read with the right device
might reveal all sorts of information
about the thing it embellished,

a pear, perhaps,
Anjou, Bartlett, Bosc
its price,
where harvested, when,
or me,
my age and weight,
propensity for failing at science
and love,
the likelihood of a long life—
a virtual fortune teller who reveals too much.

When a friend entered hospice last week
her doctors gave her only a few days—
but how many exactly?
What information do we want?
What would we rather not know?
The pear is turning too soft to eat.
Did its bar code tell when it would go bad?
Did I fail to pay attention?

This morning I found yesterday's hibiscus blossom
had already folded her petals around herself.

Reasons for Hope on the Cusp of Eighty
MJ Werthman White

The sun arises each morning as so do you.
You brush your teeth and dress yourself.

Your hips, wrists, joints, all hurt
but everything works just fine.

You've already outlived your mother
yet are no less fortune's hostage.

Your immaturity resulted in younger,
less judgmental friends. A few good pals
therefore remain to keep you company.

You still *get down*; you just can't get back up.
You are no less the fool for love.

Short-term memory loss means you get to keep
the ancient grudges you are so fond of.

And, finally, it has become clear to you
there is more good than evil in the world;

evil simply has a much better publicist.

Long Decline
Judith Fox

—after *Ejiri in Suruga Province* from the Series,
Thirty-six Views of Mount Fuji by Hokusai

Hokusai has limned the distant mountain
with a single contour line—
slow rise, scant crest,
long decline to the ground.
Gusts of wind rush
over rambling trails, tall grasses,
yank from the villagers, hats
and scarves from their heads and necks,
tissue papers from a blue kimono—
then windmill all
into a hazy yellow sky.

You, my love, stand spare and still
while deliriums of wind
down your power
lines, rip the roof from your house,
suck from the attic trunk
the red dress
I wore when we met,
a silk tie you knotted daily,
black wingtips you used to lace,
our first kiss—
then tornado us into a vast and birdless sky.

Melaluka © *Judith Fox*

Number Please
MJ Werthman White

There's a phone booth in Otsuchi in northeastern Japan
where the Japanese come to call loved ones lost in the tsunami.
Overlooking the ocean, it sits alone in a field of wildflowers.

I'd like to go there, pick up the receiver to hear an operator say
number please? and answer *long distance.* I'd like to talk to my brother,
mother, my father, to all three sisters-in-law—who does that? carelessly

loses all her sisters-in-law? I'd like to talk to friends who left me
grieving. I have questions for all who went ahead, most, unwillingly
with backward glances and sighs. *Why you, not me?* I'd ask. *What's it*

like there? Is there even a "there" there? Do you miss me? I miss you;
oh—wish you were here! as voices splinter with static and the operator cuts
in, asking for more quarters from someone whose pockets are utterly
empty.

LET ME TELL YOU WHAT IT'S LIKE
MJ WERTHMAN WHITE

Before I was old myself, cold, the black ice
of wintry simile and metaphor seemed fitting.

I was mistaken. Aging is about flame,
heat, about fires set, fires extinguished.

It's like your gas stove blows up
so you have to use the toaster oven.

The kitchen table catches fire, now
you eat on TV trays from Target.

The bed begins to smoke and char.
Suddenly, you're sleeping on the floor.

One thing after another flares, turns to ash,
until at last the house itself goes up,

with you, of course, inside. Maybe
the dog gets out. Maybe she misses you.

MY DAUGHTER'S APARTMENT
DENA TAYLOR

On the wall are photos of her sister and two nephews,
her great-great grandmother in her 90s,
a painting I did, tomatoes in a glass bowl.
I am here while she takes a shower,
not wanting her to be alone
less than 48 hours after she passed out
at the dinner table on Thanksgiving.
They couldn't find anything wrong in the ER—
stress, dehydration maybe.
But now death is on my mind:
hers, mine
all of us
of course.

SLEEPLESS
DENA TAYLOR

A song on the radio at 2am:
Sooner or later we'll all be pushing up little flowers
The chorus, over and over

I'm not afraid of death anymore
Eighty now, and a good life it's been

How much longer might I have?
One day, three years, fifteen?

It's said that soon some people
may live to be 120 but not 130
I once dreamt I'd be 137

It's something of a miracle
that we get born at all

FRONTIER
MARY HARWELL SAYLER

The dying need such simple things:
one word of care, two hands to hold,
three wine-soaked wafers
to seal the lips, the eyes.

There's nothing to be afraid of
catching or losing now—
nothing to disappoint you
from meeting this appointment
that won't be what
you might expect.

Dying is a lost art—
no matter:
uncomplicated,
unloosening each
seem.

PASSING A FARM
WILMA MARCUS CHANDLER

The farmhouse seems to lean
toward the hills beyond,
the roof mottled with afternoon sun
and only the slightest hint
of evening, thin slices of shadow
in the fields. The land seems washed
with colors of kelp and olive, bitter rich.

Whoever lives here is more than lucky.
Whoever lives here must surely have opened
to all the seasons, loved them all—
sun, storms, the constant pummel of wind.
Whoever lives here must sit, late afternoons,
on that old porch, like a kind spouse
in the turning of the years.

OUR EYES, LEFT OPEN
WILMA MARCUS CHANDLER

Not a day passes where I don't cry.
        —Gina Berriault, Iowa City, 1962

Long ago that seemed so odd—
she sitting across from me nursing a beer,
while for me everything was vivid, blithe,
straw spun daily into gold.
We were all so lavish, strong.

Later there were moments.

When introduced to your Aunt Daisy,
I was warned, "be careful, she cries all the time"
as though this were a disease.
And as she took my hand, she did and I did.
But the children all laughed.

A late-night call from the hospital 3,000 miles away:
"Your father—best get on a plane as soon as you can"
And still it was too late. After decades, always tears.

And now they arrive daily.

Tears for the pile of stained blankets
discovered under hedges in the park.
Tears for the pale baby shoe in the street,
a torn page from a diary,
a laddered nylon stocking on the curb,
for news footage of soldiers in battle gear,
elders glancing through windows,
exhausted families walking dirt roads toward a wall,

or just today, a dog left too long in a car,
who eyed me with such hope as I passed,
and then with despair, for I was not his master.

ONE MORE WEDNESDAY DINNER
WILMA MARCUS CHANDLER

For G.U.

Perhaps this is how
our days may come
to be measured.
By the distance your arm
must travel, lifting,
slowly, slowly,
pale as wax,
toward your mouth,
open, waiting
for the elaborate
meal of curry
and gingery rice
trembling in the silver spoon.
Your hand rises
another inch
then stops, suspended
in mid-air.
Eyes closed,
head tilting to the left,
a pause, a disappearance,
a going off
to small islands,
to the memory of forest, sea.
But then, yes,
your arm
rises again, an adagio,
lento, lento,
toward your mouth,
the tongue
moving now,
anticipating
the salt.

CHILDREN, WHEN AUTUMN COMES
MYRA SHAPIRO

> *To whom*
> *are we beautiful*
> *as we go?*
> —David Ignatow

Children, when autumn comes and we turn
to see the leaves, their almost too much
rouge, their topple as the wind
picks up— *A little momentum*
to remember me by, Mae West cooed,
refusing to go unnoticed—

it will be clear why fall takes
our breath away. Beauty and death
combine, and you, children, will inherit
the gold mine: Time

blessed with distance and memorabilia.

And I will appear beautiful
as I go, all yours, now always
a still life, a story
the way memory chooses to shape it.

Nature collaborates, puts up a sunset
out west with everyone traveling
towards it, wistful yet eager, wanting next.

Dearth
Myra Shapiro

Decapitation enters
my dream. *Speak*
becomes *peak, dear*
ear and *swords* give me

words. In winter death
wiped my mate away—
ate him in a way. The head
of the house he was called.

Dreams uproot to make things new,
the future tense: September,
the New Year. *Listen, witness*
how it is to be done.

How it is to be one.

Dearest Children
Kirsten Morgan

To you
who would arrive before traveling,
without passing through tangles and thorns,
to you,
sated with self-laud, easy passage and wishes
dangling for easy pluck,

because I love you,
I wish you the gifts

of senseless struggle, the clog of barricades,
treasure buried in terror.

I wish for you
as much failure,
as many lost loves, lost jobs and missed chances
as your heart can bear.

What witch of a woman would will
these fates on her dearies,
send you out
with scattered scars and hopes denied?

Perhaps, one who wants you to find gold
under dung,
one who hopes
you'll one day hear the words she can't
quite write,
words you can't yet parse.

In early years I sought out saints and sages,
Some with fractured minds and keyhole vision,
Many blinded and blundering.
Each knew the answers.
None understood my questions.
The louder they spoke, the faster I ran.

I searched every map, even drew my own,
but the ends were always dead,
and the trails dissolved in dust.

Not until eight crashed into zed,
not until I carved those numerals on my face
and laced them to my bones
could I remove the wax and sing along
with those who dwell beyond the need to know,
those who live only in this place,
this time.

My beloved children,
Now you speak in the ciphers of your tribe.
Your own world
But can't see the real life standing in full sun,
Invisible
To the quick of travel, sure of step.

All love,
Mom

LAST NIGHT
CLEO GRIFFITH

Last night you lay on the floor,
unable to rise, weak as a new-born.
The firemen who came to help said
"we have not been here for a while."
They picked you up,
placed you in your wheelchair,
left as quietly as they came, no fuss.

I know you are humiliated
when this happens to you,
you should still play tennis,
golf, drive the car, dance with me.

You cannot.
But neither can I.
Long life can be a blessing
and a curse at the same time.
We are glad to be here,
most of the time happy
for who we are.
But last night you lay on the floor,
and we both died a little more.

I Count Backwards
Cleo Griffith

I plan the winter in the midst of summer
even stretch to spring, being always aware,
not losing track, keeping an eye on the clock—
all the deadlines among all the lives,
all the dying around you and me,
that is the direction we head, feet first,
hands grip the sides of the months,
steady our gait through the slippery days,
while I count backwards from 100
each time stopping a bit sooner.

TO THE OLD WHO THINK THEY WANT TO DIE
SUSAN TERRIS

—after Gwendolyn Brooks

No! Don't unscrew the pill bottles. Stop right now!
Look—the sky is an unclouded blue above the lake.
There's a ruby-throat sampling the hosta. Whisky and
water will not help you swallow. At sunset, when you
think again about ending it all, a beaver will swim across
in front of you, as if he is returning from Toad Hall to
his own bank lodge. Are those capsules in your hand
two-toned blue? That's not your color, Sweetheart.
Instead put on your purple satin dress and tap shoes.
Then join your mirror-image and dance with her.
Hmm… are you, in your 80s, whining you're not strong
enough to chin yourself on the crossbar? Are you,
instead, considering rope? If so, make sure it's one for
jumping. You can't? Then use it for a clothesline and
let all your lace unmentionables sway erotically
in the midday sun.
        Being dead is the end of the end.
How silly when your motto for being alive has always
been *Carpe Diem*. Do you want all your little ones to wail
tomorrow if their GeeGee is gone? And you will miss
autumn's blaze, cool days when deer and rabbits turn
gray-white. Then the first snowflake, after that ice houses
on the frozen lake. Okay, so you don't ice-fish any
more. But you can make a bonfire on the beach, offer
the littles New Year's s'mores.

        So, ditch those poison pills.
Charon is not yet waiting to ferry you across the Styx.
Time is still yours. Despite all, life is, too—embrace it!

Is This How Death Will Find Me?
Sylvia Bortin Patience

Not a sudden, late intruder,
who breaks down the door at midnight,
but a well-known, familiar face?

Already we have more
than a casual acquaintance.
When we met in high school, Jim,
then later my friend Dwayne,
both ran off with Death.

Since that time we have been
formally introduced
on more than one occasion,
in professional capacities.
Our work sometimes overlaps.
At times the visits were expected,
even welcomed.

Death has met my friends' parents,
then visited my own.
Just last week Death took a job
in the office where I worked.

But this is new!
I run into Death when least expected.
Frequently the name is mentioned,
interrupting casual conversation.
People my own age,
and younger, go off without a word.

Death has moved
into my neighborhood,
could even end up being
my one remaining friend.

ORDERS
KATHERINE WILLIAMS

County Clare, Ireland

MATINS
The pink rim
of the cup of morning
holds the stippled Atlantic,
stone walls splashed with lichen,
great caramel cows under
the stretched stitched sky
where wisps of dangling threads
mark the journeys of men and women
unaware that far below
an old woman
bears witness
to their passage.

GRACE AT NOON
May she try to find thanks
for longing and for doubt
for clutter
for forgetting
for remembering   and remembering
what should be forgotten
for the promise she meant to fulfill
for not noticing
for outrage.

EVENSONG
As light begins to melt
and a faint freckle of moon
floats near the hawthorn on the hill,
she walks with the swelling weight of absence,
feels the force of her feet as they
carry her over the pebbly road,
when a car with a sheep in a trailer pulls up
and a man leans out to ask *Are ya well?*
And she answers *I am. I am well.*

Winter of the Soul
Rosaleen Rooney Myers

I feel the nectar, the bite of scotch slowly seeping through my system, warming, cajoling, tempting, the cunning desire for a drink, a drink I can't have. A drink that would begin a chain reaction of insanity if I succumb to its false allure.

I'm lying on the couch, my hands folded, my eyes closed, trying to find a stillness from the stressful thoughts in my head when that iced glass of scotch nearly pulls me to my feet and the corner bar.

That is the fierceness of my disease, but the impulse to drink has not reared its deadly head in many years. The days pass without a thought of alcohol, and if I am tired, angry, or resentful I have the tools to ease the stress and smooth my way.

But now I can't swat those thoughts away, nor find relief from the turmoil in my heart. I watch my husband take precarious baby steps across a room, a physical symptom of the weakness in his mind, or listen as he rages against the loss of himself. And I am it, his helper, his friend, his wife, his enemy.

Let go, I am told, let go, let go and find myself again. And so, I negotiate each day seeking a slice of the power that keeps me sane and serene in a strange and challenging place.

I give him his pills. Today he takes them. He empties the dishwasher. I make lunch. Today he eats. He waits for the mailman. He gives me the mail. He hands me the television remote. Today he's not sure how to use it. He sleeps in his recliner, covered in a shawl. Today he is cold.

I feel drawn by some invisible chord to escape to the west, to the sun, to the warmth of roses in the winter and the lure of the Pacific. I feel drawn to share these tenuous days of life with my little granddaughter, but that is a journey too late in coming.

It's winter. Winter in my soul, winter in the deep dark freeze of vanished light and so I sleep, curled like a cat when the sun peeks into a quiet room, huddled in its embrace like a sweet spot of peace.

LIMBO
ROSALEEN ROONEY MYERS

Limbo. The edge of hell. A place where lost souls wander the cosmos in a constant state of anxiety. That would be me, as my husband's dementia spirals down into more confusion and sadness and anger, and one hour turns to two, then three, then four as I pick up the threads of his thoughts and another day slips away into the enigma of the universe.

I reach out to touch the fragments of my life like quicksilver that vanishes at a touch and feel I am disappearing, pulled into the haze as my jaw tightens and head throbs to an empty beat. I think I shall go to Tasmania, that wild island near the South Pole to see the Southern Lights and its two moons. There I will find a small inn in the port of Hobart and wander through the market under the shadow of Mt. Wellington. I shall sit on a jagged cliff over a crystal sea or gather butterflies of rare distinction. No one will know where I am, and if I discover a Tasmanian Devil I shall tell him I am in limbo.

But for now, I need a respite, a small escape. Today the wind shears up the ocean bound streets swinging at porch chimes as the penetrating cold pushes against my down coat. Wandering into town I enter a small shop filled with sparkling jewels, soft wraps and sweaters. My eye wanders to a summer section, perhaps for those who fly south as we once did. There my eye falls upon a sandal in a silk pastel print, a delicate invitation to a brighter world. At home, I open the box and admire my new shoes, picturing them with a flowing dress on a hot summer eve as I wander through Tasmania watching the double moons rise.

THIS CANNOT BE
GLENNA COOK

My son is dying, and I sit
in my favorite chair,
drink coffee,
plan my day,
check my phone,
watch birds fly
in and out
of the budding pear tree.
This can't be.
I should cry,
raise my voice in a howl,
crumple like a discarded love letter.
A new strength courses my blood.
A new resolve grips me,
pushes me out of bed in the morning,
makes me brush my teeth as always.
The sun comes up with its usual flame,
sinks down at its appointed time.
How can this be?

SUDDENLY
JAN SEALE

Everyone is dying, going to Someplace.
I don't understand. Newly, I don't understand.
We're giving death reports to our children
the way we complained of our parents doing.
Age is knocking us up, a definite
tell-tale shade on the litmus,
formerly a speck not worth a squint.

Death's moved into the neighborhood,
made itself a welcome plate of brownies,
subscribed to the paper, built a pen for its dogs.
Lately, it's been going up and down the street
delivering letters on ways we can organize.
We're all addressed as "Resident."

ASHES ON THE AIR
LINDA NEAL

I don't remember which coat I wore, how I got to the boat, which boat, don't remember how long the long time was waiting at the dock, which time, who died, who came, who stayed, who left. Finally, pulling away from the dock, the captain said "Good morning." We were at sea.

Rose petals and ashes blowing in my hair. Ashes turning to dust, a wet mess floating on the surface of the sea. Ashes in a locked up box. Ashes in a basket, a vase, an urn, a glass compote dish. A human life distilled. Vinegar and tears. Nobody talking. Black coats, grey sky, rain blowing across the stern. Body burned into ashes and bone, floating across the sky. Ashes: people of the air. Thin, grey remnants of father, mother, husband, lover. A musky scent captured in the aftershave by the sink. His resonant bass strained through the soft cavern of his mouth hanging in the basement stairwell. A lipstick-stained cigarette burning in a bronze ash tray, an empty wine glass standing on a round teak table, two elbows and wet lips leaning in to speak. A torn Brussels' sprout lonely on the plate. Remnants. Father. Mother. Husband. Lover. A baby always crying in a windy room. It's winter and the train is rumbling through.

You can smell them in the closets and the sofas they left behind— mother, father, husband, lover—pouring down in clouds and rain and rays from sun. Guided missiles from the cosmos. From the heart. To the heart. Gone. Gone. Here, here like ancient floorboards crashing through the foundation, gone through that secret trap door, gone, wearing nothing but a scream. Here. Here, in overalls and all the colors of the long days of nights of watermelon gigs and smoked trout that tastes like escargot, all butter and garlic, on the tip of your tongue, salivating blood and the round ball of nostalgia. Fingernail clippings in the dry bathtub its four feet planted on a white tile floor.

Blue sky, blue as mountain air, bare gnarled limbs reaching, and the boy is conceived in a summer as near as my lap, and the water lap, lapping at the edge of everything. Blue lapping. Air slapping at the bow of the boat, and the bough snapping off the winter tree when the fish are hiding and the air is, yes, blue, and the woman says yes to the cabin light and the fisherman who has come in from the rain.

The last petals, pink and yellow, floating, everything floating, me floating, the water ebb-tiding around the peeling hull, and the colors of our lives blowing in the winter wind. My son standing at the top of the ladder. He sticks his hand out for me to grab, and I begin the climb back up and out.

FIELD NOTES: KEEPING ON KEEPING ON IN THE MID-80S
JULIE OLSEN EDWARDS

This body. This 85-year-old body. Bringing memories of puberty. The not knowing what strange metamorphosis my body would shift into tomorrow. Embarrassed and slightly proud—and completely awkward. Now, in the 80s—here we go again—a new list—but the same alien, visible, shifting—beyond my choice or control. Bruises, spots, discolorations, falling hair, disappearing lips, scantly-there eyelashes, thickening toes and thinning, cracking nails, drooping neck. The fat has moved from my breasts to my belly. The hair from my eyebrows to my chin.

Death walks along with me. I find myself thinking about dying, weighing my life. What I've done, where I've been, what I hoped for, where I failed. Worrying about getting ready, getting rid of the stuff that fills my house so my kids aren't drowning in the debris of my life. My lifetime gathering of stuff. It will be without meaning to those who have to clean up after me. Wanting to clear out those tangible artifacts of my life, and at the same time, wanting to hold them close.

Friends are dying. My beloved has died. There is an aloneness that shocks me and flavors every day.

Memory is unreliable. Nouns disappear leaving an itching in my brain. "I know that name! I know that word!" I can feel my brain straining, scanning, digging – "It begins with an S, it's in that song, I know it, I just can't find it!" But it's not just nouns. My memories matter more than ever. And my memory keeps morphing. "Was I in San Francisco when that happened, or had we moved to Santa Cruz? How did I get through the exhausting, overworking, hard years? How did we manage to build again after we tore apart? Did I really dance and sing the way it looks in the snapshots?"

I'm appalled I still get caught up in expectations. Glad to hear about the 90-year-old who hiked the John Muir trail by herself. Glad to know that the first-time novelist who is on the best seller list is 81. Glad there are women older than I am who look healthy, slim, and dress only in comfortable clothes and manage to look classy and snazzy and say, "I don't give a damn what I look like anymore." I am glad. Proud to see them and know them. Really. But it feels like one more decade of expectation of the "right way," the admirable way, the 'sposed to' way of being a woman, of aging. And frankly, I'm tired. I don't want to climb any more mountains. I'm not driven anymore. I move slower. I think slower. I want less (unless we're talking about comfort food...). It's time for some ease, some quiet, some moving inward, not reaching out.

TOURISTS
SYLVIA BYRNE POLLACK

Those who come back talk about
    the tunnel and the light. Details
vary, who or what they saw.
    Some insist they traveled far,
met family and God, while others,
    stayed put in the room, watched frantic
doctors thump tube-threaded flesh.

They never bring back catchy-sloganed
    T-shirts or shot glasses. Remarkably,
there's not a single photograph or
    video despite the near ubiquity
of smart phones, selfie-sticks.
    If only they would show a carousel of images
with GPS coordinates embedded.

These travelers tell us they can offer
    only words and words, they say,
are so inadequate. Still, they try,
    with glowing, rapturous adjectives.
But data-driven skeptics will avow
    these trips are just a dying brain's attempt
at making sense of the unthinkable.

That's possible and yet our minds persist
    in asking *but what if?* We and Horatio
know there are undreamed-of things.
    Why not believe the notion that a soul
goes on, its energy conserved,
    that physics and theology might partner
in a cosmic travel agency?

HER CHOICE
MAUDE MEEHAN

my own Auntie Mame

She called to say goodbye
said she was going home
She called, wanted to say thank you
for what I can't remember

My idol when I was a child
she danced her way past disapproving aunties
into a world where women were called flappers,
adventurous ones who dared
to show bare knees, to wear bobbed hair,
and in her beaded bag, a long, slim holder, gold,
for cigarettes, Gauloise from Paris
a silver flask for gin

At eighty she owned a chequered
past of roller-coastered years
furs and diamonds, an illustrious career
Bittersweet memories of a handsome
ne'er do well, then later
a steady man, ambitious as herself

She called to say goodbye, said thank you
said, you know I've always loved you
I answered be safe, you know I love you too
Call me when you come back

Later that day, all phone calls made
the mandatory notes inscribed, the time
arrived for sweet relief of hoarded capsules

downed with a crystal glass of finest Scotch
She left with the same panache
as she had lived her eighty years

There were those who called it selfish;
as for me those last few years
I could scarcely bear to see
her spirit fade, dwindle
like her waning world.
Goodbye old girl, and I say Bravo

Part Eight

Women's Wisdom

The most courageous act is still to think for yourself. Aloud.
—Coco Chanel, 1883-1971
French fashion designer, international businesswoman.

Trust yourself. Create the kind of self that you will be happy to live with all your life.
—Golda Meir, 1898-1978
4th Prime Minister of Israel,
first and only female head of state in the Middle East.

The idea of winning a doctor's degree gradually assumed the aspect of a great moral struggle, and the moral fight possessed immense attraction for me.
—Elizabeth Blackwell, 1821-1910
British and American physician,
first woman to earn a medical degree in the United States.

Lives that flash in sunshine, and lives that are born in tears, receive their hue from circumstances. None of us know what a year may bring forth.
—Harriet Jacobs, 1813-1893
American author and activist,
writer of *Incidents in the Life of a Slave Girl.*

O WISDOM! if thy soft control
Can sooth the sickness of the soul,
Can bid the warring passions cease,
And breathe the balm of tender peace,
WISDOM! I bless thy gentle sway,
And ever, ever will obey.
—Anna Laetitia Barbauld, 1743-1825,
English essayist, poet, children's book author, & editor.

CRONE STAFF
SYLVIA BORTIN PATIENCE

Gray owl feathers
downy soft for silent flight.
Great bird of the night,
of the darkness and dream time,
gray like the strands
which run through my hair,
symbol of the crone passage already made.

Dry white bleached bone,
spines outspread.
The bird takes flight
on the final crossing into darkness.

Bird woman dancing.
Dance of life.
Dance of joy.
Intricate dance of relationship,
of sameness,
and of difference.

These symbols tied to the redwood staff,
the crone staff.
Smoothed and oiled by loving hands,
no longer young and soft,
not yet stiff with age.
Hands of the crone in her power,
retaining her blood,
gestating wisdom.

Secret power of the crone,
this passionate fire that still burns,
after being wives to men,

having birthed and loved our children.
Transforming fire,
destroying old patterns,
dead wood on the forest floor,
making way for new growth.

Living on as crone,
gray owl woman.

CURIOSITY
PATRICIA LeCLAIR

If I turn my head to the left, I can see the spiders' house.
    A daddy-long-legs has designed
A thorough and complicated web on the inside of my lamp
    shade. It is a messy and tangled
Affair. She guards this territory upside-down from the upper
    left hand corner. She has a tiny
Dark comma of a body. Her 8 legs are pale, almost translucent,
    with little white hinges, each
Leg forming an incomplete rectangle. She hangs completely
    motionless for days at a time.

I don't know much about spiders, how often they need to eat—
    or HOW they eat. When no
Flies are caught in her web for days, I begin to toss newly
    swatted flies into the lamp shade.
She speeds to where the fly has landed; swiftly and certainly
    wraps it up; holds it for a day or
So then drops the wrapped husk. She is done. I am not.
    I continue to drop dead or dying flies
Into the maw of her web until some days later I realize what
    folly this is.

I gently capture my friend in a container with a lid. I take her
    to a vacant corner of my front
Porch and I open the lid. Now she has built a new web. There
    are lots of flies out here, more
Than she can eat; however she eats.

I am an old woman, I want to live this old age with curiosity,
    I want to look at the small things
I overlooked before, I want to live with grace and dignity.

MEDITATION
PATRICIA GRUBE

I have been sitting here for an hour and a half just dreaming. I thought I was meditating but that drifted into worrying. Whatever it was, it seems I need a kick in the butt to get me started doing whatever it is I plan to do today. This morning I am thinking that loneliness is a major theme at this time in my life. Like a big bird it swoops in and takes all the air out of the room. Putting words on paper does not make it go away. If I can make friends with this creature, I think it will be better than getting a dog.

A Short Bio
Patricia Grube

Right at the beginning I need to level with you.
I was a child who believed in Santa Claus
and wouldn't listen to anyone
who said that Santa was a lie.
I wanted to believe in the Easter Bunny
although the idea seemed incongruous.

I was quite old when I figured out
there was a baby in the fat lady's tummy.
I began to worry and wonder
how it would get out.
Quite a while later I wondered
how did it get in.

These things didn't occupy
much of my mind's time
for I was learning about
the continents and the peoples
of the world, the ancient wonders
and the lives of the saints.

I had a child's eye view of prohibition.
I often heard the men in the family
discussing their recipes for home brew
and on several occasions
I was awakened by the explosion
of bottles in the cellar.

I was first aware of the miracle of radio
when my uncle who lived down the block
and was something of an inventor
came running to our house

to call my folks to come and listen,
"I've got Denver on the air or Dallas
or somewhere far from Phoenix."
I heard a king give up his throne
a great influence on my romantic nature.
I heard a reporter describe the explosion
of the Von Hindenburg dirigible.

I enjoyed Amos and Andy
and never thought of them as black or white.
They seemed like two of my uncles.
I loved Jack Benny and would throw
a tantrum if Mama called me to dinner
in the middle of the Lux Radio Theatre.

Once my Dad took me to a field
outside of Phoenix where we watched
an airplane make landings. The pilot
offered rides to anyone brave enough to try.

I was twelve before we had a refrigerator.
There was always an ice box;
when the ice man came to deliver
a twenty-five or fifty pound block of ice,
we kids would chase after the truck,
begging for chips of ice.

Dad fought in the war to end all wars
and then there was another war.
My brothers went off to fight.
One was killed in France in the same
region where my Dad was injured.

I married a young Lieutenant
who had just received his wings.
Those were the days when death
was our constant companion.
I have lived on the edge of despair
and of happiness
and sometimes
both at once.

SUDDENLY I'M OLD
PHYLLIS CHESLER

Suddenly, or so I'm told, I'm "old," a "senior" citizen.

Who, me? When did this happen?

Just yesterday, or at least before a series of illnesses and surgeries, I was filled with energy and physical strength. I'm now walking-disabled and use a walker and/or a cane.

Once, I joined some schoolmates from long ago at a restaurant. I looked around and kept looking around—astounded that those white haired women who looked "old" were once girls with whom I attended New Utrecht High School back in the 1950s.

They looked "old." But not me. Over time, I acknowledged my aging only in terms of my health—pain, agony, surgeries, and the inevitable medication strips.

People tell me that I look a decade younger than I am. Frankly, given all the wars I've fought and continue to fight, I should look a decade older!

But oh! I am increasingly robotic, and when I still traveled, I was always patted up and down rather intimately at airports, because my non-organic parts invariably set off alarm bells.

Other than very occasionally forgetting someone's name for a few seconds, or sometimes for a few minutes, my brain is just fine, still very much on fire. In this, I am very lucky. What matters most to me, what takes up most of my time, is my reading and writing and thinking. That's who I am, that's where I live, and where I feel most alive. Although I have bad days, sometimes any number of bad days, I have not slowed down all that much.

Come the fall of the 21st century, I turned sixty. Since then, I've published ten books, thousands of articles, and delivered hundreds of lectures.

But when I turned 75 in 2015, I stopped traveling as much as I once did (too arduous, even in an airport wheelchair), and with the pandemic, I stopped going out all that much. I can't hold my own in a crowd or in dreadful weather. Interestingly, once I started using a walker,

I realized that it served as a protective barrier as much as a walking aid with a seat.

Before, I had not realized how many people do not see where they are walking as they talk on their cellphones or listen to music—even mothers with babies in strollers are busy texting. I began to feel vulnerable. I came to see the walker and the cane as defensive devices, meant to signal vulnerability, but it rarely makes a difference. I usually have to step aside for others on the street.

I've had Covid twice and long Covid as well and don't want them again. Thus, I'm anxious about sitting too closely to others, even if they're masked; can no longer wait on too long a line for the bathroom; cannot get to all those places that have too many steps without someone along with me to lift my walker.

I *can* meet someone in a restaurant or at their home if a car service takes and returns me.

In short: It's my body, not my mind, not my ideas, that have slowed me down. In my case, not in all cases, my leading a rather sedentary life, one of an academic, an intellectual, a writer—meant that I betrayed my body.

I also lived my life as if it would never end—and did not build nest-eggs of any kind, neither in academia, in publishing, in movement, or financially. I just kept moving on, focusing on ever-new subjects, refusing to till and then guard a single garden of expertise. One pays a price for acting as if one can continue to satisfy one's curiosity, take on ever-demanding missions, without having been born wealthy.

As for myself, I am a "daughter of earth," a daughter of Jewish immigrants, and on my father's side, a first-generation American. I was named after my paternal grandmother who was slaughtered by Cossacks in her tea shop in Lutsk, Ukraine.

But, I am also exceptionally lucky. As an American girl, I obtained a good education, had many careers (professor of psychology, feminist leader/activist, author, researcher, part-time psychotherapist, consultant). I was always able to support myself.

I led a life surrounded and guided by books—and, when I was thirty-seven and a half, I became a mother. Giving birth to a living being is miraculous. My son, born just yesterday, is now a Supreme Court judge. I am definitely very proud of him. He is a feminist. In a sense, he was "mothered" by an entire generation of Second Wave feminist leaders with whom he dined, and to whom he listened, talked, and shared holiday tables.

My son has given me a wonderful daughter-in-law, and two beautiful granddaughters. Most of all, I have been living with a very successful lawyer, a woman, for 31 years (I finally gave up on men—not all men, just the men I chose as lovers and husbands).

My partner is someone who protects and supports me in all the ways she can. On my own, like so many other feminists and aging or uncoupled women, I'd be relatively impoverished, living in an assisted living facility of some kind, alone, probably miserable, unable to do my world-work. Alas, our imagined feminist communities, feminist old age homes, have yet to come into being.

What wisdom might I have to impart?

First, never stop telling the Emperor that he has no clothes on. Always speak truth to power—but do not expect to be loved or supported for doing so. Expect friendly fire, but personalize nothing. Whatever happens, it is not just about you.

Second, please understand that, like men, women are also sexists and highly aggressive and competitive but mainly towards other women. They also collaborate with men in patriarchal practices. Thus, watch what a person, male or female, does, not just what they say, and try to choose your friends and allies carefully. Of course, this is not always possible.

Third, try not to reduce or balkanize your identity. You are more than one thing, more than whom you might sleep or live with. Like Walt Whitman, we each contain "multitudes." If you only salute one ideological flag, belong to only one tribe, it will be difficult, perhaps impossible, to create coalitions of people for the common good.

Fourth, don't follow the crowd, especially not if they are cruel and mindless or even evil. Understand that if more good women stand up to tyrants, the fewer tyrants there will be.

Fifth, please realize that life is a God-given gift, a treasure. Practice gratitude.

Sixth, be kind to others. Respect other women. You do not have to love them.

Seventh, may I dare to suggest that you read some of my books? For example: *Letters to a Young Feminist, Woman's Inhumanity to Woman, An American Bride in Kabul,* and *A Politically Incorrect Feminist.*

IN THE 91ST YEAR OF MY LIFE
GITTA RYLE

I was born on April 10, 1932, and am writing this in the 91st year of my life. For the last 28 years, and continuing to this day, I have been speaking in schools, sharing my story of how I as a child survived WWII and the Holocaust. Doing this has given me a positive purpose. I try to share how I learned to forgive but never forget. I no longer have to hold in my mind and body all the negative thoughts that I had throughout my childhood. I am no longer a victim.

At this time of my life, I am grateful for each day. I appreciate all the things I can do on my own. I am content with my life and pretty much at peace. I have learned that what happens in the world I have no control over. I do what I can to make life better where I can. I have learned to be a good listener and have empathy, especially for our youths.

I keep fairly busy and active, and I still live alone but have wonderful neighbors. I hope for peace and for human beings to learn to love themselves and savor life.

OLD AS DIRT
JOAN STEINAU LESTER

Don't prioritise your looks my friend, as they won't last the journey.
Your sense of humor though, will only get better with age.
    —Dame Judi Dench

"Fuck the kids," Laverne snaps, peering at her phone to read a text. She shoots me a conspiratorial look, but with a tinge of something I can't read. Does she wonder how the others in our new group—five women all facing 90—will respond to "fuck"? "That's Rose's and my saying whenever our grown kids bug the shit out of us," Laverne explains, compounding the problem if there is one. "When we're trying to get some distance. This is from Hector, my son. He's on my case. 'Mother,' he said. That's what he calls me when he's going to reprimand me. 'Just listen and don't say anything.' As if I'm a two-year-old. And even then, that's no way to speak to a child. 'It's time for you to face facts and think about moving.' Who the fuck does he think he is, telling me what I should think about?" She slaps the phone on the table, reaches for a deviled egg, and stuffs it into her mouth.

The Elliott Houses where we first met back in the '50s were red brick towers, new public housing stuck out in a deserted part of Chelsea, way over by the West Side Highway. It was heaven. No rats like in my former apartment, where we heard scratching in the walls and had to cover our faces from the stink every time they died. The projects hardly even had roaches. Vito and I, with our baby Diego, were one of the few white families—or nearly white. Well, conditionally white, depending on the day and who was deciding. Vito DiCello, a dark-skinned Sicilian, straddled the line, confusing the hell out of everybody. As a Jew, I too complicated the picture. But Vito and I were white enough for our Black neighbors to classify us that way, even if most neighborhoods excluded Jews back then. That "otherness" has been the story of my life. Maybe that's one reason Laverne and I bonded so strongly. She and Booker lived next door, big readers, which is how we first connected. It's hard to believe that sixty years later we landed near each other again, all the way out in Oakland, California. Not in public housing, either.

"Hector's working my last nerve," Laverne tells the group, speaking loudly. As her hearing's declined her volume has gone up. "'Have you thought about what you would do if you have another heart attack, Mother?' Uh, yeah. How does he think I made it to 90? I do still have a brain. Does he think congregate living is a guarantee against heart attacks? Actually, I bet statistics would show the reverse. All that stress of institutional life! Or worse yet, moving in with him and his nasty wife. Now that would be a disaster in the making. It would take about two days to shoot my blood pressure through the roof." She laughs, fusses with her hearing aid, and pops another deviled egg. With her cropped white hair she looks radiant, powerful in her Ghanaian smock. "I feel like an African queen," she had told me the day she'd tried it on. No way is Hector going to force this queen to move.

"Young people think they know everything," Toni Wong says with her lop-sided smile, a mix of bemusement and resignation. She must have perfected it in the courtroom. Small, compact, female, and Chinese-Chicana to boot, I can only imagine how the judges or opposing lawyers treated her 60 years ago when she started out as a lawyer.

"I was such a believer in the Chinese revolution," Toni continues. "My father was ethnic Chinese even though he grew up in Mexico, so I felt a connection. I thought the revolution meant that starving peasants like his ancestors wouldn't have to sell their children every time there was a famine. I was out on the San Francisco streets every week cheering Mao. I practically memorized the Little Red Book, sabes. 'Let a hundred flowers bloom.'" Toni stops, shakes her head and scowls. "So maybe cut Hector some slack? People always think they know way more than their parents. Especially their mothers."

"Oh, but Hector knows everything," Laverne mocks in her lovely deep voice. "Last week when I said something about pot, he rebuked me, 'Mother, it's called *weed.*' As if I didn't know. That's why I say, 'Fuck the kids.' They better show some respect."

The words feel deliciously heretical—after all the years I spent obsessing about my children. Twenty-five years of my life, three kids with three fathers, and most of that time trying to make it on my own. I don't know how I did it. I never got to express my resentment or despair until Laverne and I invented our chant a few years ago.

Hazel Harrison, who owns this house, says. "My three sons are making the same noises about me moving. They say, 'With your vision, Mom, how can you live here? We'll help you into assisted care. Or move in with one of us. It's not safe anymore to live alone.' You're right, our kids are all reading from the same booklet. It's as if once you turn 90 all your adult children are issued a Boot-Your-Mother-Out-of-Her-Home pamphlet."

Detta, our fifth SuperCrone who's busily knitting and hasn't spoken much, adds without looking up, "Bless their hearts. Well, y'all, Lupe, my goddaughter, knows how I feel about those 'Senior Living' places. Goodness gracious, all these glitzy brochures showing happy straight couples. Shoot me first."

Every time Detta speaks, that white Southern drawl takes me right back to 1960 when I watched little Ruby Bridges on TV in her starched dresses and Mary Janes walk the gauntlet. A six-year-old with a bow in her hair who needed federal marshals to guard her on the way to first grade! Yet every day she returned with her entourage: four burly white men with badges ushering her through the hateful New Orleans crowd. Spitting at a child!

Detta has a story, for sure. She introduces herself through clenched teeth. "I'm a writer… who's not writing since my partner of fifty years died. She passed four months ago." Detta looks as if she could scream, but as soon as she finishes speaking, she bends her head to her knitting, refusing to make eye contact with anyone.

In Toni's email inviting me to this new group, she'd already named us the SuperCrones. "Doesn't crone mean ugly old woman?" I emailed back. She replied, "Crone was once positive, like 'witch.' Crone comes from crown, indicating wisdom from the head. But during the Inquisition, they took those words and turned them around. I'm wanting to reclaim them. Like we reclaimed 'queer.'"

Now Toni looks affectionately at Detta, who says, "I told my goddaughter, 'I'd rather stick needles in my eyes than move.'"

She grimaces.

"I *have* had needles stuck in my eyes," says Hazel. "Ever since I started losing my eyesight, I go every three weeks to a retina specialist.

The shots slow down the process of going blind, so I'm glad to get them. I'm 91, the oldest one here, I think." She swivels her head, checking us out. Wow, that makes her the doyenne of the SuperCrones.

"I wonder, gals," Detta drawls, "when I turn 90 next week if my god-daughter will turn up the heat. 'Buy a condo in Florida,' she tells me. 'I'm here four months a year and you could live next door!' She's driving me nuts. Florida is the last place on earth I'd want to live. The politics. The heat. The homophobia. Over my dead body. Pretty soon it will be my dead body," she laughs. "Then she can move her dear old Mama wherever the hell she wants. Bury me, cremate me, throw my ashes into the sea, I don't care. Meanwhile I'm staying put. I love my little carriage house on Haight Street. Thank God my partner and I bought it after twenty-six years of renting. And it's paid up."

Despite our differences, what we have in common is our advanced age. It seems like we're going back in time to our childhoods, when the only condition for a friend was to be the same number of years old. You assumed you'd find similarities. "Life is circular like that," Toni says.

"What's your favorite part of being 90? Or about to be?" she asks. After a few minutes of silence Laverne begins, "When I wake up and I have absolutely nothing on the calendar that day. It feels spacious. I'm taking pleasure in the little daily moments I never had time to enjoy before. All the years I was Ron Dellums' Chief of Staff, working for a Congressman is 24/7. Now I get to see what I missed when I was rushing around. I settle down with a book for a couple of hours before I go outside to weed the garden. Or take a walk. It's lovely."

Hazel muses, "I can sleep in as long as I like. For forty years I worked as a horse trainer outside in every kind of weather. Up early, stay late. And I loved every minute of it. I wrapped wounds on the horses' legs, cleaned their sores, groomed them, comforted them when they hurt. I just wanted to take good care of those magnificent creatures. I wasn't living any more as a woman trying to look good or please other people. I got stronger every day. But this right now, this is just as good. In its own way." She pauses. "My work was hard physical labor. Especially in the last years. But now I'm living the dream. Mostly that's doing nothing, staying inside warm and cozy. My family and friends make sure I have anything I need. That's the good part of being so old—people do

268

look out for you."

"*Yo Hago Lo Que Me De La Gana*," Toni sings. "*I do whatever I want.* That's the name of a Bad Bunny album. Maybe you're channeling him."

"Bad Bunny?" Hazel asks.

"He's hot, he sings about how everyone wants to be Latino but they lack *sazon*, that Puerto Rican sauce."

"What a name, Bad Bunny."

"That song sounds like you—*I Do Whatever I Want.*"

"It's true," Hazel chirps. "I'll have to listen to that song. Bad Bunny. That's funny."

I Have No Wisdom
Claire Braz-Valentine

Each time we age into a new decade we face biases and expectations. Once we turn 30, we begin to accept we are not children anymore. Turning 40 we feel we have reached full on adult status. Turning 50 is another experience, not always a good one. This is about the time we find ourselves beginning to wander down the cosmetic aisle of the drug store, trying to decide on either a moisturizer or a line filler.

Add another 30 years onto that and then one day you look in the mirror and think, what the hell happened? I need to buy some stuff!

In one of my poems, "The Last Will and Testament of This Woman to Every Woman," written when I was in my 30s, I gave away all my pancake makeup, my blusher, my rouge, my eye shadow... well, I think I want them back now.

According to television advertising, when we are in our 80s, we have become the night of the living dead and just to top it off, with our hip and knee replacements, we are limping a little, looking for the remote when it's actually in our pocket, and we are wondering if the wrinkle resurfacing facial pads are really worth the trip?

We can refresh our complexion with an ultrasonic pore extractor, this is after we have plumped our lips and exfoliated our face to remove dead skin, sort of like sanding down a house before a paint job.

In the US we spend over 49 billion dollars in cosmetics sales each year but that's understandable because where else are we going to get our salicylic acid or our hyaluronic serum?

That stuff doesn't grow on trees and when we turn 80 it's time for us to do our part to support this industry because they have our best interest at heart, and point out that wrinkles are not our friends.

The problem with being in our 80s is not only how we look, but people expect a certain amount of wisdom because we are the elders, and frankly I don't have any wisdom to impart. When I was a young woman, I said I wanted to grow old with gusto and I wanted younger women to celebrate their age, rather than trying to cover it up.

But I find that being in my 80s is much different than being 40 and thinking about being 80. There are situations I have to encounter just to defend myself. Take driving for instance, where an old lady behind the wheel brings out the ugly in the bullies driving giant pickup trucks.

So, I am not driving fast enough?
To you road hogs I want to remind you that
I am someone's Grandma.
I am five someone's grandma and one person's great grandma.
And I have been paying taxes since before you were born, jackass,
so the fact is,
I own more of this roadway than you do!
As you cut me off, and flip me off, you don't scare me!
For over 30 years as a workshop leader in Arts in Corrections,
I have sat in prisons
without any guards in the room and I shared stories
with maximum security inmates doing life
without the possibility of parole
and I have called them my friends,
and you with no respect, flip me off
because I'm not driving fast enough for you?
Let's just agree that I would never take your photo and paste it online where any inmates who want to, can see it! I would never even think of doing that, but perhaps you should think about it.

Along with encounters on the highway I have to deal with the checker
at the local grocery store who always greets me with
"Well hello young lady," and if I buy a bottle of wine,
he makes a big deal of asking if I'm old enough to drink.
I know he thinks he's being cute or funny or clever except
I want to slap his scumsucking smile off his stupid face.
I try to be the sweet little old lady but I am not sweet, not little,
and I am a woman, not a lady.
I don't think references or comments about my age are necessary
or anyone's business.
My new tiny dog agrees with this attitude.
He was rescued wandering around in a parking lot.
And when I adopted him, I was told he was 4 years old.
He just looked at me with his big puppy eyes

and agreed.

It seems though, according to recent reports from the veterinarian
my sweet little 4-pound puppy has been lying about his age
and as I was picking him up from the doggie dentist, sans 4 teeth,
I was told he probably was at least twice the age I thought he was.

So now my dog is going grey and so am I.

As I get out the root touch up, I tell him he just has to deal with it
but I don't.

Once I heard that Ruth Bader Ginsberg colored away her grey.

I headed back to the hair care aisle at the drugstore.

If it's good enough for RBG,

it's good enough for me.

But the fact is that my family doesn't like talking about age.

When I was a child, I was told don't ask anyone's age or their weight.

My mother married three times and she was ten years older
than the final two
and they died 10 years before she did.

When my oldest son went into the hospital for knee surgery when he
was in college the nurses announced to me that "girlfriends" are not
allowed in the patient's rooms.

I assured them that the beautiful young man in the bed was in fact
my son.

They had me prove it with my license.

Suffice it to say the reason my family does not discuss age is because
we have been passing for much younger our whole lives.

I have been asked if I have had a face lift, Botox injections,
scrapings or fillers and the answer is no.

I was born with an aversion to sunlight.

I sat in the sun once when I was 16, and I hated every minute of it.

I have always said I am more the mushroom type.

I like damp and shady places.

Sun is not my friend.

I was born and raised in San Francisco and fog to me is a blessing.

A windy foggy day is lovely

So now I am in my 80s and the age issue has become a HUGE BIG deal.

People expect stuff from us 80-year-olds.

How do I want to be remembered?

What guidance do I want to give to younger women?

Words by themselves are just words.

If you want inspiration for your life's path from me

then judge me by my actions, along with my words.

Know that I marched against every war

was a member of Mothers for Peace

got my young-looking nose maced

raised three wonderful feminist sons

kept my brother and sisters as my dearest closest friends

demonstrated for equal pay for women and

marched with Cesar Chavez along with the farm workers.

I organized women's consciousness raising groups

and did psychodrama in the '70s.

I changed my protest sign from *Another Mother For Peace* to

Another Grandmother for Choice.

I got spit on protesting for women for choice

in front of Planned Parenthood.

I had my plays (all about women's lives) produced in four foreign

countries and off Broadway in New York.

I am now expected to have some words to live by.

I'm not sure I have them.

When I was in my 80th year

three of my beloved friends died within a few months of each other,

and I was actually going to marry one of them. He asked me.

I said yes. He went home and had a heart attack and died.

Then because of the fire that destroyed my little cottage in the woods

in my little town of Paradise, I retired from most of my prison work

because I didn't know where I would be living month to month and

my nerves were shot anyway.

To the flames I lost every poem I ever wrote and so many blessed

friends sent me copies of my work and this particular one

probably says it all about aging that I need to say,

REMEMBER

Remember, this is not a sad song
I am one of those one out of five Americans who can remember
    World War II.
I helped my mother wrap fruit cakes to send to Uncle Roland in Iwo Jima
We poured cool brandy…a whole bottle…on the cake.
That was 1943
I was four
I was born in the last year of the thirties
I am a thirties original
A good year
A vintage child
I am not an imitation.
I really did live through blackouts in the Mission District in
San Francisco after the bombing of Pearl Harbor
We had no TVs. We worried those days in front of big radios.
We had no computers, no laptops, no cell phones
Our house phone had only four numbers, 4623, it was a "party" line
And we could lift the receiver and hear someone else's private phone call
We sat on overstuffed couches which we called chesterfields.
This is no apology
But we had no instant coffee, no instant breakfast, no instant oatmeal
To play our 78 records we had to wind up our phonograph
Instead of plug it in because there was no plug.
And I was not deprived
I went to high school in the fifties
I took Latin like a good Catholic girl
And I made out in the back seat of cars
I went to pajama parties
I loved Elvis Presley
I went to my junior prom in a strapless formal and wore a corsage
    tied to my wrist
I had fun. I had fun
And laughed forever.

I married young and frightened and afraid I was pregnant.
I bought a chrome dinette set and had an upright mangle ironer
    and I ironed socks.
Three babies came and became my sons and became my eternity
and helped me to pretend I was okay
    even though I took them from their father
    even though I waited tables in the night to feed them
    even though they cried a lot
I am so very proud of them.
I moved them up to a home in the mountains
    under the trees.
And if all of this makes me old
I am old. I am old. I am old.

***

I have to admit though that those trees cut our house in half
    and then in the next home in the forest, the trees caught fire
    and burned up the whole town.
But still nothing in nature makes me happier than a tree or the ocean.
Of course, trees give shade and the ocean gives fog
Those are two of nature's gifts that this 83-year-old woman loves.
If I could give advice for anyone,
    plant a tree and keep our ocean pure and your families close
    and lie about your age if you want to and
I suggest you stop worrying about how you look,
    it's what you do that counts.

No Recipe
Patricia Grube

there is no recipe
to put together
the layers of my life

some are delicious
both in making
and consuming

some are hard and heavy
frosting will not
hold them together

maybe toothpicks
will keep everything
in place

the problem is that
nothing can be discarded
does this have to be a rule

yes because some layers
made me strong
and others made me free

First, You Need to Lose Nearly Everything
Maria Mazziotti Gillan

First, you need to lose nearly everything—
all the people you've loved—
your husband, mother, father, all the aunts and uncles, sister, cousins,
your best friends of forty years, a parade of other friends
most at least two years younger than you.
All those cremations and funeral bouquets
of hothouse flowers that begin to die so quickly,
it's as though they are anxious
to join those wax people wearing their fanciest clothes
in their mahogany coffins,
their heads resting on satin pillows,
although many of them never owned a satin pillow in their lives.

Second, you need to shed years as quickly
as a dog sheds hair,
Time, that bright ball, rolls steadily downhill
so that each second moves faster than the one before.

Next, you have to stop believing you are invincible,
that death is for other people, but not you,
and then your body starts to betray you
all the things you used to be able to do
are no longer possible or easy
like yesterday when I tried to lift my foot in high boots into the car,
and I couldn't manage, so a man in the street
came over to the car and helped me get in—
I wanted to be cool, so I was wearing lace up combat boots
and even those I will have to relinquish.

But this morning, the peace of the Retreat House
wraps me in a shawl of soft cashmere

and the poems make the mansion glow
as though lit by one thousand candles
and outside, the sun has emerged for the first time in days
and the trees are beginning to soften into spring.
So much I have lost, but this is how to learn gratitude—
though so much is taken, so much beauty remains.
I celebrate the first crocus pushing its way out of the frozen ground,
the patterns that the sun makes on brick walls,
the words that spring to life in the solarium at Saint Marguerite's
    Retreat.
How happy they make me.
How grateful I am for all that I've been given
and all that remains.

Contemplating Work in Old Age
Angie Boissevain

Each dish I know, and touch as I touch
my own hands and face, the forks know me,
the bed's opening and closing is part of a story.
When I tend the garden, the garden
tends me, and when I go inside,
my pockets filled with oranges,
juncoes' and bushtits' conversations
still fill my mind.
I am so happy to be able to work, to act, to do.
I love to touch, pick up and move things.
I love to go up and down the stairs.
I feel so lucky to be digging up the iris,
sweeping the walks, plowing garbage
into the mulch pile. What a great life,
to be still living like this!
You might call it work. I call it a fortune.

Persimmon Top Pendant by Fereshteh Fatemi

Contributor Biographies

JANICE ALPER, originally from Brooklyn, New York, has had many lives—among them: daughter, wife, mother, speech therapist, Jewish communal worker. Now, happily retired in La Jolla, California, she spends her time writing personal essays, poems, and memoirs. Her work has appeared in *The San Diego Poetry Annual, San Diego: A Year in Ink, The Jewish Writing Project,* and other places. Janice's latest publication is *Sitting on the Stoop: A Girl Grows in Brooklyn, 1944-1957,* available from Amazon. You can follow her at www.janicesjottings1.com

HENRI BENSUSSEN'S writing comes out of the world of nature; she converses with carpenter bees, fence lizards, spiders in a bathtub—the flowers and trees she meets while hiking. She has a B.A. in Biology from UC Santa Cruz. A chapbook of poems, *Earning Colors,* published by Finishing Line Press, came out in 2015. Other poems and short stories have been published in a variety of journals. She is hoping to find a publisher for her memoir, titled *The Transgressive Heart.*

ANGIE BOISSEVAIN was born in the Midwest and has lived life-long in the San Francisco Bay Area. She raised three boys, tended a house and garden and helped to found Jikoji, a Zen Buddhist retreat center in the Santa Cruz mountains. When fully ordained, she brought Zen meditation practice to centers in Europe and the U.S. for many years. Now retired, she lives in San Jose, CA, and can be reached at boistree78@att.net and +1 408-677-4894.

CLAIRE BRAZ-VALENTINE has never been happy writing in just one genre. "Perhaps I have been fickle, bouncing from children's stories, to humorous feature articles for adults, to plays for children, to adult theater that has been produced in five countries and translated into many languages." In addition, she spent 30 years conducting writing workshops in maximum security prisons for incarcerated male inmates, three years writing a play with the women of Chowchilla Prison, and another two years writing a play with incarcerated drug addicted juveniles. "This 'work' has filled my heart. I raised three magnificent sons as a single mother and I now have five magnificent grandchildren and one great grandchild who is magnificent also!"

JACKIE BROOKS is now 87, retired from college teaching, and a stint in the Peace Corps in Madagascar where she taught English. She has published stories and poems in literary journals and small presses. Her novel, *The Ravenala,* set in Madagascar, was published in 2013 and can be found on Amazon.

WENDY TAYLOR CARLISLE writes poetry in the Arkansas Ozarks. She is the author of four books and five chapbooks and is the 2020 winner of the Phillip H. McMath Poetry Award for *The Mercy of Traffic*. Her first book, *Reading Berryman to the Dog*, was reissued by Belle Point Press in 2022; *Discount Fireworks* can be found reprinted online at doublebackbooks.wordpress.com and a chapbook-length selection of her work appears in *Wild Muse: Ozarks Nature Poetry* (Cornerpost Press, 2023). Find more at www.wendytaylorcarlisle.com.

SHEILA CARRILLO explored innovation in education while raising her children, helping to found Evergreen School in Ben Lomond and Dos Alas Spanish language immersion program. She produced bilingual multi-cultural events and co-founded Peace Day, celebrated at Mission Plaza Park (1985-1995). Politically, her focus has been in the area of social justice, including alternatives to police, compassion and care for our homeless neighbors, people and environment over profits in housing and city planning, and justice for Palestine. She co-founded The Muslim Solidarity Group, participated in Sanctuary Santa Cruz, and currently is active in the Welcoming Network and Santa Cruz Palestine Solidarity. She began writing and publishing political commentaries in her seventies and is surrounding herself with a food forest.

WILMA MARCUS CHANDLER was born in Manhattan and grew up on Long Island and in the Adirondacks of upstate NY. She is a playwright, poet, theatre arts and dance educator. Her books on theatre scholarship have been published by Smith & Kraus, Inc., and she has taught Theatre and Dance at the University of Iowa, University of California Santa Cruz and chaired the Theatre Arts Department at Cabrillo College in Aptos, California, for many years. She has directed well over 100 productions in the Bay Area. Her poetry collection *The Night Bridge* was published by Hummingbird Press. Among other events, she co-founded the *8 Tens@8* International Short Play Festival, The National Festival of Women's Theatre, My Kin Talk, a Jewish Women's Readers' Theatre Company, and "In Celebration of The Muse" Women's Writers Festival which has been produced annually for over 40 years. She can be reached at: wilmakchandl@gmail.com.

PHYLLIS CHESLER, Ph.D, is an Emerita Professor of Psychology and Women's Studies, and is the author of twenty books. She has introduced or contributed to more than eighteen anthologies and has penned thousands of articles. Her books include the landmark feminist classics *Women and Madness* (1972), *Mothers on Trial* (1986), *Letters to a Young Feminist* (1998), and *Woman's Inhumanity to Woman* (2002); *The New Antisemitism* (2003), *An American Bride in Kabul* (2013), which won a National Jewish Book Award, *Living History: On the Front Lines for Israel and the Jews 2003-2015* (2015), *Islamic Gender Apartheid: Exposing a Veiled War Against Women* (2017,) *A Politically Incorrect Feminist*, and *Requiem for a Female Serial Killer* (2020). Her work has been translated into many languages, including French, German, Dutch, Italian, Swedish, Portuguese, Polish, and Russian, and into Japanese, Chinese, Korean, Hebrew, and Arabic, and has been cited in academic journals on every continent. Since 9/11, Dr. Chesler has focused on the rights of women, dissidents, and gays in Hindu, Sikh, and Muslim communities; the rights of women in prison; the rise of anti-Semitism, the demonization of Israel; the nature of terrorism, forced veiling, forced marriage, polygamy, and tribal psychology. She has published four studies about honor killing. Based on this academic work, she has submitted affidavits for Muslim and ex-Muslim women who are seeking asylum or citizenship. In 2021-2022, she co-led a team which rescued four hundred women from Afghanistan. That work continues. She has archived most of her articles at phyllis-chesler.com. She is a co-founder of the Association for Women in Psychology (1969) and the National Women's Health Network (1975) and a founding member of "Scholars for Peace" in the Middle East, the Academic Freedom Alliance, and the anti-Islamist Clarity Coalition. She is a Senior Fellow at the Investigative Project on Terrorism; a Writing Fellow at The Middle East Forum, and a Fellow at the Institute for the Study of Global Anti-Semitism and Policy, and is also a founding member of the original "Women of the Wall."

JUDITH COHEN's novel *Seasons* was published by the Permanent Press of Sag Harbor, New York, and is still in print. Excerpts appeared first in the *New American Review*. The book was originally published in German translation by Rowohlt of Hamburg as part of their international *New Woman* Series and has been reissued as an eBook. Her short fiction collection *Never Be Normal* (2021) is available from Atmosphere Press. Her stories have appeared in numerous magazines including the *North American Review, New Letters, High Plains Literary Review,* and others. In March 2023 Judith was the featured writer on Alphabetbox.com, and her story "High Peaks" is in Choeofpleirn Press' *Coneflower Cafe,* Spring 2023. Her latest essay called "Underwhelmed in Cuba" is in *The Berlin Literary Review,* Issue One, May 2023. She is a retired college professor (Lesley University, Cambridge, Massachusetts) and teaches yoga at a Senior Center. Email: Markanjudy@msn.com

GLENNA COOK, a widow in her eighties, recently moved from her long-time home in Tacoma, Washington, to an apartment in a senior community in nearby Puyallup. Diagnosed with Parkinson's Disease ten years ago, she maintains a disciplined lifestyle with regular exercise to slow down its progress and is an advocate for others with this disease. She has been writing poetry since attending college in her fifties and graduating from the University of Puget Sound with a B.A. in English at age 58. She has published two collections of poems through MoonPass Press: *Thresholds* (a finalist for the Washington State Book Award for Poetry) and *Shapes of Time,* and is now well into her third. Glenna is a mother, grandmother and great-grandmother. Her outlook on life is: "We make our own weather."

LAURIE CORN was born in Toledo, Ohio, lived in Jerusalem, Israel, and studied at Roosevelt University in Chicago. She resides in Santa Cruz, California, and has two children. She is a radio producer and artist and writer. Her published memoirs include: *The Half-Built House on The Hill: Marriage, Motherhood, and Madness, The Two Gents and I: A Tale of Two Brothers and The "Last Rites" of a Jewish Father,* and *Pilgrimage of the Ancient Tortoise: A Tale of Septuagenarian Love.*

CONSTANCE CRAWFORD was born in California in 1930 and majored in English at Stanford University where her short stories won various prizes including *MLLE Magazine* Fiction Contest. She continued writing fiction, married, and had four children. After divorcing in 1967, she earned an M.A. in Psychology and spent several years as a group counselor. Her memoir *The Muse of Menus: Stories from Life and Cooking* was published in 1988. For the last 20-odd years Crawford has studied the writing of poetry with poet Ellen Bass. She lives in Palo Alto, California.

JUDY DAVIDSON is a recently retired Marriage and Family Therapist who provided counseling to county employees, spouse/partners and teenagers. Her past careers included working as a Benefits and Employee Assistance Program Manager for a local newspaper and as a substitute math teacher in local high schools.She wrote the equivalent of an, as yet, unpublished "how-to book" for caring for one's aging parents. She was a frequent contributor to *70 Plus: A Literary Journal for Seniors by Seniors.* Judy has always done personal writing for insight and for fun and used this experience to design and teach a popular class called "Write On! Writing for Fun and Health." She currently participates in a bi-monthly writer's support group that "keeps her writing." When she is not writing, you can often find her out on one of her beautiful local hiking trails. Email judydsierra@gmail.com

JULIE OLSEN EDWARDS was a member of the Child Development and Women's Studies faculties at Cabrillo College, Aptos, California, for over 45 years. Consultant/writer/union organizer/good trouble-maker. Co-author of *Anti-bias Education for Young Children and Ourselves.* Still a mom, now a widow. Hanging in at 85.

ROSANNE EHRLICH has written works published by Ballantine Books, *Chicken Soup for the Soul, Persimmon Tree Magazine,* Quillkeepers Press, *True Grit Anthology, Fredericksburg Literary and Art Review, Viewless Wings Poetry Podcast, Fifty Word Stories* and others. She has also written and produced episodes for *The Great Ships* series on the History Channel. Non-fiction work and poetry have appeared in many small magazines including *Metafore Magazine, Antirrhinum Journal* and *Glitter Literary Journal.*

RHODA MAE EVANS was born in Hoboken, NJ. She migrated to the Pacific Northwest during the Seattle World's Fair in 1962. She holds an M.F.A. in

Performance Art from the Art Institute of Chicago where she also taught 4D Time Arts, incorporating film, photography, poetry, sound and video into her performances and installations. She performed with Seattle's Dappin' Butoh for three years and her photographs have been exhibited in Seattle galleries and printed in Contact Quarterly. Her poetry has appeared in *Fine Madness, Port Townsend Minotaur, Hoboken History, The Fib Review* and *Raven Chronicles Memorial.* She lives in Seattle where she earned a living remodeling houses and as a hospice program assistant.

FERESHTEH FATEMI is an Iranian-American artist with a bachelor's degree in Fine Arts, and master's degrees in Interior Architecture and Spiritual Psychology. She had a 30-year career in interior design for international hotels and restaurants. Her passion for creating art and hand-made objects inspired her to try numerous techniques, including her most recent creations in silver and gold jewelry, watercolor mandalas, and fused glass pieces. In her poetry, she is consistently inspired by her love for Rumi and his philosophy. More about Fereshteh and her work is at: ferangelika.com and on IS: @ferangelika

JUDITH FETTERLEY is a former Distinguished Teaching Professor of American Literature, Women's Studies, and Writing Studies at Albany / State University of New York. She is the author of *The Resisting Reader: A Feminist Approach to American Fiction* and *Writing Out of Place: Regionalism, Women and American Literary Culture.* Since leaving her academic appointment, she has owned and managed a small garden business, "Perennial Wisdom" and become a Master Gardener for the Albany County Cornell Co-operative Extension. She currently writes a bi-monthly newsletter, "Out in the Garden," which can be read and subscribed to on her website, perennialwisdom.net

JUDITH FOX is a poet and fine art photographer. She's a finalist for the *2023 Bellevue Literary Review* John & Eileen Allman's Poetry Prize and BLR's Spring 2022 Poetry Prize. Her poems also appeared or are forthcoming in *Rattle, Notre Dame Review, Sugar House,* and numerous other journals. Fox's photographs are in the collections of six museums including LACMA, the Virginia Museum of Fine Arts, and the Harry Ransom Center at the University of Texas, Austin. Her photography book *I Still Do: Loving and Living with Alzheimer's,* was named "one of the best photography books of 2009" by *Photo-Eye Magazine.* Photographs from *I Still Do* were exhibited around Europe and the United States and Fox has been a global advocate and speaker on behalf of Alzheimer's awareness and family caregivers.

ALICE FRIMAN's eighth collection of poems, *On the Overnight Train,* is a New & Selected published by LSU Press. Her last books, also from LSU, are *Blood Weather, The View from Saturn,* and *Vinculum,* which won the Georgia author of the year award in poetry. A recipient of two Pushcart Prizes and included in *Best American Poetry*, she's won many prizes and has been published in *Poetry, Ploughshares, Plume, Georgia Review, Gettysburg Review, Crazyhorse, Poetry East, Massachusetts Review*, and many others. Her website is alicefrimanpoet.com.

MARIA MAZZIOTTI GILLAN is a recipient of the 2014 George Garrett Award for Outstanding Community Service in Literature from AWP, the 2011 Barnes & Noble Writers for Writers Award from *Poets & Writers*, the 2008 American Book Award for her book, *All That Lies Between Us* (Guernica Editions), founder/executive director of the Poetry Center at Passaic County Community College in Paterson, NJ, and editor of the *Paterson Literary Review*. She is also a Bartle Professor and Professor Emerita of English and creative writing at Binghamton University-SUNY. Her most recent books are *When the Stars Were Still Visible* (Stephen F. Austin State University Press, 2021), the poetry and photography collaboration with Mark Hillringhouse, *Paterson Light and Shadow* (Serving House Books, 2017) and the poetry collection *What Blooms in Winter* (NYQ Books 2016). Others include *The Girls in the Chartreuse Jackets* (Cat in the Sun Books, 2014); *Ancestors' Song* (Bordighera Press, 2013); *The Silence in an Empty House* (NYQ Books, 2013); *Writing Poetry to Save Your Life: How to Find the Courage to Tell Your Stories* (MiroLand, Guernica Editions, 2013); *The Place I Call Home* (NYQ Books, 2012); and *What We Pass On: Collected Poems 1980-2009* (Guernica Editions, 2010). She is co-editor of four anthologies with her daughter, Jennifer. Her poetry website: www.mariagillan.com. Poetry Blog: mariagillan.blogspot.com. Artist website: mariamazziottigillan.com.

JILL GINGHOFER —"I was born and raised in the Southern English town of Bournemouth, known for its balmy climate, palm and pine trees, all a rarity in the cold of Britain. I've lived in Santa Cruz for the past 50 years, also a town renowned for its balmy climate, palm and pine trees. Here I had a marriage, three loving children, and righteous work. Before arriving in Santa Cruz, I lived all over and belonged all over."

JEANIE GREENSFELDER's poetry has been published in *American Life in Poetry, Writers' Almanac*, and Poetry Foundation's *Poem of the Day*; in anthologies: *Paris, Etc., Pushing The Envelope: Epistolary Poems*; and in journals: *Miramar, Thema, Askew, Persimmon Tree* and others. She served as the San Luis Obispo Poet Laureate 2017-2018. Jeanie's books are: *Biting the Apple, Marriage and Other Leaps of Faith*, and *I Got What I Came For*. Visit jeaniegreensfelder.com

CLEO GRIFFITH, 87, lives in the poetry-rich Central Valley of California and delights in the community of artists of many disciplines. She finds relevance in every facet of her life and is grateful for the extra value poetry brings to her in these later years. Cleo has been on the Editorial Board of *Song of the San Joaquin* for twenty years and her poems have recently appeared in *Wild Roof Journal, Lothlorien,* and *POEM.* She is on Facebook and can be reached online at cleor36@yahoo.com.

PATRICIA HERNAN GRUBE was a playwright and poet from Santa Cruz, California. She died in 2022 just before her 99th birthday. She was born in the desert of Arizona and moved with her family to California when she was eleven. Her education at the University of California, Berkeley, was interrupted during World War II. Later she received degrees in Sociology and Psychology from the University of California, Santa Cruz. She published three books of poetry: *The Green Door, Layer by Layer,* and *Then and Now.* She also wrote a book of short stories about the 2 years she spent in Zambia, Africa, with her husband and children. A number of her plays have been produced, including *Grandpa's Breakfast, Falling Apples, Found Wanting, Relative Shades,* and *Twilight.* In her writing she sought to find drama and transcendence in the lives of ordinary people.

JOANNE HALE was born and educated in Oakland, CA. The oldest of 7 children, she has three children and four grandchildren. She received M.Sc. degrees from University of California, Davis (International Agricultural Development), and from Stanford University (Applied Economics). She served four years in the Peace Corps in the Philippines as a High School Chemistry/Physics teacher (2 years) and as a rice production specialist (2 years). Worked and lived full-time in Africa, Asia, and the South Pacific for 34 years—Philippines, Papua New Guinea, Sri Lanka, Bangladesh, Indonesia, Malawi, Uganda, Nepal, and Uzbekistan. Short term assignments for the Bill and Melinda Gates Foundation and the U.S. Dept. of Agriculture, and long-term assignments (23 years) for the U.S. Agency for International Development. Adjunct professor at Santa Clara University for 5 years. Personal email: JoanneByWeb@gmail.com.

JAN HARWOOD —"I published my first of two political/mystery novels, *Dangerous Women* and *An Un-Conventional Murder,* when I was eighty and eighty-two, when I had time for such delightful things, after a long career as a psychiatric social worker and raising three very cool kids. I've always written humorous verse and, under the brilliant tutelage of the poet Ellen Bass, many autobiographical short stories. I've also scribbled hundreds of lyrics for my gaggle of political protest singers, the "Raging Grannies." Now, at age ninety-two, my poems are more expressive of my need to praise this marvelous, fragile planet and its natural works of art, from clouds and redwoods to the gorgeous critters in the deep seas. Coming soon: *Patchwork: Stories from My Life.*

ANN HOWELLS edited Illya's *Honey* for eighteen years. Recent books are: *So Long As We Speak Their Names* (Kelsay Books, 2019) and *Painting the Pinwheel Sky* (Assure Press, 2020). Chapbooks include: *Black Crow in Flight,* Editor's

Choice in *Main Street Rag's* 2007 Competition and *Softly Beating Wings,* 2017 William D. Barney Chapbook Competition winner (Blackbead Books). Ann is a multiple Pushcart and Best of the Net nominee; her work appears in many small press and university publications.

PATRICIA HUKILL lives in Oakland, California, having moved across the bay from Palo Alto in 2022. Acclimating to a community of over 200 people has been a challenge. She has been writing "Morning Pages" since the '90s when Julia Cameron's *The Artist's Way* came out. In recent years, the process has become a conduit for the Muse to send poems almost daily. Around 2016, she published many poems in *The California Quarterly* and now sends monthly poems to the community newspaper at Piedmont Gardens, *The Crest.*

BARBARA JOANS, Ph.D., was the author of numerous articles on anthropology, feminism, and women motorcyclists, and the book *The Changing Woman: Women of a Certain Age.* She was also the recipient of many honors and awards for her work in anthropology.

JULIANNE JOHNSON has lived in Manzanita, Oregon, for more than 30 years. As a sun-seeker she would happily replace the chilly, wet weather of Manzanita. However, the community is irreplaceable. Hence, she stays. And galivants to sunnier climes from time to time.

MARGIE KERN-MARSHALL was born in 1930, of Ukranian and Romanian heritage. As a child, she lived in the home of her Romanian grandparents in Los Angeles, along with her parents and four uncles—all eking out a living during the Great Depression. She earned her Masters in History (and taught history of the "New Colonies"). In the 1960s, Margie and her first husband, Hartley, sojourned in twelve countries in Europe, Asia, and Africa, working at everything from dishwashing to teaching. Years later, after settling in Santa Cruz, California, with her new love, Lee, she taught English, first for migrant worker families, and eventually as Chair of the English as a Second Language department at Cabrillo College. She was a union organizer, and was active in the ACLU and the UFW. Margie was one of the founders of "First-Person Singular," a radio program where locals can air a story or a political rant. One of her radio pieces is presented, in written form, for this publication.

JOYCE KIEFER grew up and raised her family in the San Francisco Bay Area, attended San Jose State and worked for many years in administration at Stanford University. There she did interviews for the oral history project of the Stanford Historical Society. "I've seen incredible changes over the years but find that a number of things remain the same. I enjoy writing about both." Her short stories, poems and creative non-fiction have appeared in various anthologies and in the

San Jose Mercury News. She also writes a blog about her travels and her discoveries in everyday life—lifeinthepursuit.blogspot.com, and can be contacted at jfkiefer@gmail.com.

ROSIE KING was born in Saginaw, Michigan, hometown of Pulitzer winner Theodore Roethke, her first live poet, whose sister she had for 9th Grade English. A graduate of Wellesley College, she came west for graduate school in the '60s and taught beginning poets at UC Santa Cruz while finishing a doctorate on the late poetry of HD. Her poetry has appeared in various journals and seven of her poems were read by Garrison Keillor on NPR's Writers' Almanac. Her first book, *Sweetwater, Saltwater,* was published in 2007 and her second, *Time and Peonies,* in 2017, both by Hummingbird Press. With the kind encouragement and keen eyes of longtime poet friends, she has another as yet untitled in the works. When not traveling, she lives in a house she first landed in fifty years ago with a garden near the beach in Santa Cruz.

PATRICIA LECLAIR writes "I think when I measure my life now, I do not want to be fixed in time or encumbered by things. I want to be filled with light, jubilant with it. I want to be weightless, elusive, living in the exhale." She is a retired psychotherapist, 83 years old, and does not do electronics. She can be reached at +1 831-761-1647.

JOAN STEINAU LESTER's excerpt is from a novel-in-progress. Dr. Lester is the PEN award-winning author of six books (fiction, memoir, biography, and essays). Her social commentaries have aired on "All Things Considered," "Marketplace," and "Perspectives," and published in the *Los Angeles Times, CNN, Chicago Tribune, San Francisco Chronicle, Common Dreams, The Washington Post* and many others. Find out more about her and her latest book, the memoir *Loving Before Loving: A Memoir in Black and White,* at her website: JoanLester.com. She loves to hear from readers at JoanLester@JoanLester.com.

NANCY SMILER LEVINSON is the author of *Moments of Dawn: A Poetic Narrative of Love & Family, Affliction & Affirmation,* as well as a collection of poetry, *The Diagnosis Changes Everything.* Her work has appeared in numerous journals and anthologies, including *Hamilton Stone Review, Constellations, Burningword Literary Journal, Dreamers, The Copperfield Review, Schuylkill Valley Review, Panoply,* and *Journal of Expressive Writing.* In past chapters of her life, she was a journalist, editor of education books, Head Start teacher, and author of some thirty books for young readers. She lives and writes in Los Angeles.

DEENA LINETT lives on the Gulf Coast of Florida, where she grew up. She has published four novels and five collections of poetry, the most recent *When I Was Water* from Tiger Bark Press. At present she is working on a book in the voices of women over 80 in the arts and the poem in this anthology was written by one of the characters in that manuscript.

GRACE LINN, a centenarian, quilter, feminist, computer programmer, and social activist, lives in Florida. The publicity in 2023 surrounding her "Targeted and Banned" quilt can be found in her interviews with MSNBC, the Paramount Network, YouTube, and on many other sites. Her impassioned address to the Martin County School Board against censorship brought her national media attention, and she has been subsequently engaged as a spokesperson for the Velshi Banned Book Club.

PERIE LONGO of Santa Barbara, California, Poet Laureate (2007-09), likes to say "Poetry is my life," and she is most grateful for it. She has published four books of poetry, the most recent *Baggage Claim* (2014) as well as others in literary journals including *Connecticut Review, International Poetry Review, Nimrod, Paterson Literary Review, Prairie Schooner, Rattle,* and *South Carolina Review.* She leads poetry workshops for the Santa Barbara Writers Conference, has taught poetry through California Poets in the Schools for many years, and facilitates poetry workshops privately. A psychotherapist, she leads poetry writing workshops for healing and is Poetry Chair for the Nuclear Age Peace Foundation. Website: perielongo.com. email: perie@west.net

CAROL McMAHON was born on a very cold December 22, 1936, in Idaho, left home after graduating high school early to go "East" to a university on a scholarship, and later, worked in San Francisco, leaving only to ski in Austria during Christmas vacation. "It was so wonderful, I stayed in Europe for the next 55 years! During that time, I married an American, raised two sons in the German school system, completed my doctorate in clinical psychology, taught psychology at a university, set up a private therapy practice, and served as the primary caregiver for my husband until he died eight years ago. It was during the isolation of caregiving that I wrote stories inspired by my experiences. Two years ago, I decided, while I was still able (!) to return to the US, where I have a son in Scotts Valley, California, and granddaughters in Los Angeles. I now live in a senior residence where I share my passion for art weekly in a lecture series with a loyal following of the residents and facilitate a discussion of end-of-life issues monthly for members of the local Senior Center. I enjoy each day studying languages, writing, and taking online university seminars." Comments or questions are welcomed: carolmcmahon36@gmail.com

HERMIE MEDLEY entered Willamette University in Salem, Oregon, in 1938, majored in English, and wrote one poem before she received her Bachelor's degree. She didn't write another for 25 years until she began taking classes at Gavilan College in Gilroy, California. She continued to write ever after with work appearing in many magazines and *The Anthology of Monterey Poets*. *Being Human* and *Too Young to Be Wise*, two books of her poetry, were published by Many Names Press in Santa Cruz, California.

MAUDE MEEHAN. In the middle of her sixth decade, Maude Meehan moved from the East to the West Coast, accidentally stumbled into a writing class, became part of the writing group that grew from it, published four anthologies with that group, followed by numerous volumes of her own, gave writing workshops for many years, and was a popular University of California Santa Cruz guest poetry teacher. Being adventurous and fearless is what made it possible for Maude to become a writer, but her unique insights into the kindness and cruelty, beauty and ugliness that she witnessed in her life are what make her worth reading. She was honored in 2001 by Poetry Santa Cruz for "her inspiration to poets of all ages." Her books of poetry include *Chipping Bone, Washing the Stones, Before the Snow,* and *As If the World Made Sense.*

DEENA METZGER is the author of 20+ books, 7 of which are poetry. Her latest poetry books are *The Burden of Light* (2019) and *Ruin and Beauty: New and Selected Poems* (2009). Her latest novels are *La Vieja: A Journal of Fire* (2022), *A Rain of Night Birds* (2017), and *Feral* (2011). *La Negra y Blanca* won the 2012 PEN Oakland Josephine Award for Literature. The novel *The Other Hand* (1999) asserted that the Bomb and the Holocaust were the two koans of the twentieth century. Her classic writing book, *Writing for Your Life* (1992), is still in print and popular. Metzger co-edited *Intimate Nature, The Bond Between Women and Animals* (1998) with Linda Hogan and Brenda Peterson, which pioneered the radical understanding that animals are highly intelligent and exhibit intent. She has been teaching writing privately since she left Los Angeles Valley College, California Institute for the Arts, and the Writing Program that she started at the Woman's Building, Los Angeles. Within the last years, she developed "Literature of Restoration," focusing on forms and language that generate ethical concerns and restoration of the natural world (https://literatureofrestoration.org/). For the last twenty or more years she has been teaching "19 Ways to a Viable Future For All Beings," a guide to how we change our minds sufficiently to live differently and act in ways that will preserve the future and protect the earth and all beings. deenametzger.net/19-ways. Her current essays are posted on *Desperate Love Letters for a Wounded Earth* substack.com/@deenametzger. She is currently working on a new novel, *The Broken Lambs.*

KIRSTEN MORGAN has taught poetry to children in an independent school, elders in a lifelong learning program, and clients of "The Gathering Place," a day shelter for homeless and impoverished women. She is a longtime member of Denver's Lighthouse Writers Workshop, has published in many literary journals, and was a finalist for the Birdy Prize from Meadowlark Press. She is the author of *Without Skipping a Beat: A Child's Heart Transplant Journey,* editor of *One Day, One Night at a Time: Women Write of Poverty, Homelessness and Hope,* and co-editor of *An Uncertain Age: Poems by Bold Women of a Certain Age.* Her chapbook, *Inside Out,* will be published in 2024 by Poetry Box Press. She hikes, snowshoes, reads incessantly and writes prose and poetry delightedly, both in Denver and snuggled into her house deep in the mountains.

BONITA ANNE MUGNANI is a spiritual advisor and creator of ceremonies, celebrations and rites of passage. She was co-facilitator of women's artist communities and, as an educator, developed programs for children teaching science curriculum through art. Bonita is a performance artist with a passion for ritual theatre and has performed original one-woman shows. She is also co-founder of Peace Day Project and co-creator of multi-cultural festivals called "Peace Day: Discovering Our Common Ground" in Santa Cruz, California, which received a United Nations Peace Messenger Award for local peace efforts and community events. Bonita currently lives in Santa Cruz, California.

ROSALEEN ROONEY MYERS, a graduate of Ramapo College of New Jersey, is the author of *Herself, Agnes in America, The Secrets of Beacon Hill,* and the memoir, *Uncle Raymond's Garden.* She is also co-author of *Three Brown Eyed Girls,* all available on Amazon. Her short story, "Death at the Queen," appeared in the anthology *Darkness Falls at the Jersey Shore.* Her short story, "The Dark Magnet," won first prize in *East Meets West American Writers Review.* She began writing when she retired, but has a history of being involved in the communications field. As a young woman she worked at ABC News in their documentary unit and then as Assistant to the President. While raising two children she entered Ramapo College of New Jersey and received a degree in Communication Arts with honors. Subsequently she became the Development Director for a large non-profit. She has self-published four books and her work has appeared in *American Writer's Review* and received an award for best short story. Rosaleen is a widow and lives in the seaside town of Ocean Grove, New Jersey, a National Historic District, the template for Quest for the Bower. She served on the board of the Historical Society of Ocean Grove and is the Vice President of the Shore Action League, a philanthropic organization. She is also a member of the Jersey Shore Arts Center.

LINDA NEAL. Writer, meditator, therapist, teacher, wife, mother, divorcee, widow, dialysis and transplant patient, Linda Neal is the daughter of an engineer and a pin-up model. She grew up in the south Bay Area of Los Angeles under the spell of *The Wizard of Oz,* Marilyn Monroe, James Dean and The Bomb. Over the years she has founded and run several reading series and led writing and meditation workshops. She holds an MFA from Pacific University in Oregon. Her poems and memoir pieces have been widely published in many print and on-line journals, including *Calyx, Chiron Review, Crosswinds, Lummox, Prairie Schooner, Tampa Review,* and *Thimble.*

ALICE NEEL 1900-1984. American artist known for expressionist portraits depicting friends, family, lovers, artists and strangers. Her work is in permanent collections that include the Hirshhorn Museum and the National Gallery of Art, Washington, D.C.; the Metropolitan Museum of Art, the Whitney Museum, the Museum of Modern Art, New York City; and the Tate Gallery, United Kingdom.

NAOMI NEWMAN has been a concert singer, television actor, improvisational theater director and psychotherapist. For over three decades with A Traveling Jewish Theater, she changed hats between director, playwright and performer, winning awards in each field. For contributions to the cultural life of the Bay Area she received a Tikkun Award, Mill Valley Creative Achievement Award and Theatre Bay Area's Community Leadership Award. A book containing an oral history of her life and career is now in the Legacy Collection of the San Francisco Performing Arts Museum. Her work is included in: *Being Bodies, Callings, The Feminine Face of God, The Living Workplace, The Performers' Guide to The Collaborative Process, Uncoiling the Snake; Women of Power, The Spiritual Art of Being Organized, Persimmon Tree, Exchanging Voices: a Collaborative Approach to Family Therapy,* and *The Quotable Woman: The first 5000 Years.*

JEAN NORDHAUS's six volumes of poetry include *Memos from the Broken World* (Mayapple Press, 2016), *My Life in Hiding* (Quarterly Review of Literature, 1991), *The Porcelain Apes of Moses Mendelssohn* (Milkweed Editions, 2002), *Innocence* (Ohio State University Press, 2006), and *The Music of Being* (Broadstone Books, 2023). Her work has appeared in *American Poetry Review, The New Republic, Poetry,* and *Best American Poetry.* She has served as poetry coordinator at the Folger Shakespeare Library, President of Washington Writers' Publishing House, and for eight years as Review Editor of *Poet Lore,* the oldest continuously published poetry magazine in the United States. Additional information and links to poems can be found at: poetryfoundation.org/poets/jean-nordhaus Email: jfnordhaus@gmail.com.

GUNILLA NORRIS lives in Rhode Island. *Old and Singing* is her fourth book of poetry. Her second book, *Joy is the Thinnest Layer,* won the Nautilus gold prize for the best collection of poetry in 2017. She is also the author of several books on the spirituality of the everyday. Visit her website: GunillaNorris.com

SYLVIA PATIENCE is a mother, grandmother, nurse, and midwife, in Santa Cruz, California. Her writing helps her interpret her experiences with birth and death, and what comes in between. She has had poems published in *Calyx, Porter Gulch Review, La Gazette,* and *The Anthology of Monterey Bay Poets.* She has published two novels for children, and a third, *The Double Crossing,* is new from Paper Angel Press. Email sylvibo@cruzio.com, website: sylviapatience.com

MARGE PIERCY. Knopf published Marge Piercy's 20th collection of poetry, *On the Way Out, Turn Off the Light,* and before that, *Made in Detroit.* Her 17th novel is *Sex Wars. Dance the Eagle to Sleep, Vida,* and *Braided Lives* were reissued by PM Press with introductions by Piercy; also short stories *The Cost of Lunch, etc.,* and *My Body, My Life* (essays, poems). Her memoir is *Sleeping With Cats.* She has given readings, speeches, and workshops in over 570 venues here and abroad. www.margepiercy.com. Box 1473, Wellfleet MA 02667

SYLVIA POLLACK. The work of Sylvia Byrne Pollack, a hard-of-hearing poet and former scientist, appears in *Floating Bridge Review, Crab Creek Review, The Stillwater Review,* and many other print and online journals. A two-time Pushcart nominee, she won the 2013 Mason's Road Literary Award, was a 2019 Jack Straw Writer, and a 2021 Mineral School Resident. Both her debut full-length collection *Risking It* (2021) and her new collection *What Lasts* (2023) are from Red Mountain Press. Visit her at www.sylviabyrnepollack.com.

SIMONE RENAUD was born in France but lived in Casablanca, Morocco, until 1946. Studied and taught French to foreign students in Paris and Geneva, Switzerland. Moved to Hawaii in 1959. Taught there and later in Eugene, Oregon. Married, had a son, and raised two stepchildren and one adopted daughter. Moved to San Jose, California, in 1964, and taught at San Jose State University. Wrote French textbooks and retired in 1979. Moved to Soquel, California, in 1981.

BERNICE RENDRICK lived on a weedy acre in Scotts Valley, California, with many visits from deer, wild turkeys, friends and family. At 93 there was no plan, "every day just happens." Poems surprised her. She returned to Cabrillo College, Aptos, California, at midlife and published many poems in literary journals and also read many times at "In Celebration of the Muse," the women's literary festival in Santa Cruz.

MARILYN REYNOLDS is an author and retired high school teacher who lives in Sacramento, California. Her first book, *Telling,* was the first of eleven books in her *True to Life Series* from Hamilton High. Her book *Till Death or Dementia Do Us Part* chronicles her journey with her husband from 2009-2014. Other books include *Over 70 and I Don't Mean MPH* and *Over 80—Reflections on Aging,* published by New Wind.

SHIRLEY RICKETT belongs to the old bunch in that "I've been writing since the '70s." My publications include *A Minute of Arc* (Dam Poets Press), *Dinner in Oslo* (Aaardvark Global Publishing), *Love: Poems on Vintage Song Titles* (Finishing Line Press), and *Transplant* (Flowersong Press). *New and Selected Poems: Cicada* will be available soon. She holds an M.A. in Education and one in English

Literature from University of Missouri, Kansas City, and her poetry has been nominated for a Pushcart Prize. She has led workshops at the Writers Place in Kansas City and the Valley International Poetry Festival and other venues. She now lives in South Texas and is most proud of her book *Dinner in Oslo,* a chapbook based on the interviews with the adult children of Nazis.

ELIZABETH RIVERS. Chosen as the Montgomery County, Pennsylvania, Poet Laureate for 2008 by Marie Howe, Elizabeth Rivers is also the 2009 winner of the Robert Fraser Open Poetry competition sponsored by Bucks County Community College. Author of three poetry books, she enjoys bringing creative poetry writing to children, working with individuals on the internet and in classrooms. You can contact her at elizrivers@aol.com

MARILYN ROBERTSON. Poets are a lot like gardeners, always trimming and transplanting, picking what's ripe and ready, or else waiting for the seeds to grow.

GITTA RYLE was born on April 10, 1932 in Vienna, Austria. She, with her sister, was one of the many hidden Jewish children in France. She is now an in-demand public speaker and is active in her community. She resides in Santa Cruz, California, and can be reached at: gittale@comcast.net.

IRENE SARDANIS is a retired psychologist, born in New York to Greek immigrant parents. She has been published five times in *The Sun Literary Magazine,* in many anthologies and most recently in 2016 in *The Magic of Memoir.* She has been invited to read from her memoir chapters and has attended writing conferences in San Miguel de Allende, Mexico; Key West, Florida; Mendocino, California; and the Catamaran Writers' Conference at Pebble Beach. She has attended classes with Elizabeth Fishel's Wednesday Women's Writing, Louise Dunbar, Mark Greenside, and several workshops with Laura Davis. She resides in Oakland, California.

MARY HARWELL SAYLER has been reading and writing poems since childhood, but, as an adult, wrote almost everything except poetry. After placing fiction, nonfiction, and devotional books with various publishers, she began submitting poems to journals, anthologies, e-zines, and, eventually, book publishers, who accepted four of her poetry books. Later, she collected many of her previously published works along with new poems in *A Gathering of Poems* (2020) and *Haiku Happening* (2023), found on Amazon.

JOYCE SCHMID is a grandmother and psychotherapist living with her husband over half a century in Palo Alto, California. Her poems have recently appeared in *New Ohio Review, The Hudson Review, Five Points, Literary Imagination,* and other journals and anthologies. Contact info: +1 650-321-9238.

PATRICIA L. SCRUGGS is the author of one poetry collection, *Forget the Moon*. Born in Colorado, she spent ten formative years in Alberta, Canada, before taking root in Southern California. Patti still sometimes uses English spelling. Her work recently appeared in *Burningwood, MacQueen's Quinterly, Inlandia, ONTHEBUS, Spillway, Rattle, Rip Rap, Cultural Weekly, Crab Creek Review,* as well as the anthologies *13 Los Angeles Poets, So Luminous the Wildflowers,* and *Beyond the Lyric Moment.* A recent Pushcart Prize nominee, Patricia is a retired art teacher who earned her MFA at the California State University, Fullerton. She and her husband of over 60 years are parents of two and grandparents of three.

JAN SEALE, the 2012 Texas Poet Laureate, is a writing generalist, with nine books of poetry, two of short fiction, three of nonfiction, nine children's books and four stage plays. Her latest book is *Particulars: Poems of Smallness.* She is the recipient of a National Endowment for the Arts Fellowship in Poetry. Jan lives on the Texas-Mexico border.

MYRA SHAPIRO's poems have appeared in many periodicals and anthologies including *The New Yorker* and two editions of *The Best American Poetry.* She is the recipient of the Dylan Thomas Poetry Award from The New School and was the finalist for the Robert H. Winner Award from the Poetry Society of America. Her books of poems are *I'll See You Thursday, 12 Floors Above the Earth, When the World Walks Toward You;* and the memoir, *Four Sublets: Becoming a Poet in New York.* Shapiro serves on the Board of Directors of Poets' House and teaches poetry workshops for the International Women's Writing Guild.

TILLY WASHBURN SHAW. By birthright, a New Englander. Tilly Shaw came West in mid-life to join the literature faculty at University of California, Santa Cruz. When younger she published three books on modern poets and then began writing poetry herself. A graduate of Swarthmore with a doctorate from Yale in Comparative Literature, she lived in Santa Cruz with her fruit trees, friends, writing groups, and books and did lay counseling with seniors. She swam in any ocean she was able.

ADELE SHEDIAK'S imagination was captured by the cadence of the psalms and the classical music which filled the house when she was a child, the gift of an immigrant father who came to the United States from Syria in 1908. Throughout life she's had a poetic sense and wrote poetry beginning in elementary school. She is grateful for the vibrant community of which she became a part after moving to Santa Cruz in 1989. She's awed by the natural beauty of the area and inspired by writing retreats held on the magnificent Big Sur coast. Currently her muse is sparked at the annual Poetry Festival held in the high country of Yosemite, by her daily walks on East Cliff, and by her neighbor's cat, Hope, who challenges Adele's attempts to make her a feline friend.

LUCILLE SHULKLAPPER. Born on May 5, 1934, I began writing poetry, music, and fiction from the age of six, but never published until I was sixty. In the past almost three decades, my work has appeared in anthologies, literary journals, five chapbooks, and a picture book. I wrote little in my seventies after the death of my husband. The poems in this anthology were written in my eighties. I explored Stream of Consciousness in *Til There Was You*. Lucs34@aol.com

JUDITH ORTIZ SHUSHAN is a retired university lecturer in English and the Humanities, educated at University of California at San Diego. After retiring, she returned to her native New Mexico to embark on a new career as a creative writer. "Though I have had several short stories published, including 'V.E. Day' in the Penguin anthology, *Catholic Girls* (1992), I now have the freedom to pursue my passion, novel writing, full-time." She grew up in 1940s Gallup, New Mexico, and at eleven, her family moved to Los Angeles, "a completely different world culturally, geographically, and historically. It was an abusive family situation which I dealt with by joining a Chicana gang, then I ran away at age 14, worked in a record factory, married a businessman, became a radio announcer, had three children, and for a time played the role of glamorous, sophisticated wife. Throughout all this time, literature and stories were my passion and my anchor. In the late '60s, I 'Tuned in, Turned on, and Dropped Out,' which included getting my education so I could raise my children independently while working in the field I loved. As a single mother and full-time student/teacher, I had little time to seriously write with publication in view. But I never stopped writing. I collected my short stories in a gallery novel called *Beaner Blue*, and when I retired to Santa Fe, I was free to do what I'd always wanted: Just write."

CAROL STONE is Distinguished Professor of English and creative writing, emerita, Montclair State University. She has published five books of poetry, among them *Traveling with the Dead*, Backwaters Press, and *American Rhapsody*, Cavankerry Press. Her recent work has appeared in *Blue Fifth Journal*, *Slab*, and *Bellevue Literary Review*. She won three fellowships from The New Jersey State Council on the Arts and a Fellowship from Hawthornden Writers Retreat, Edinborough, Scotland. Her most recent book, *Limited Editions*, will be published by Cavankerry Press, November 2024.

DENA TAYLOR is the author of *Exclamation Points: Collected Poems* (Many Names Press); the co-author, with Becky Taylor, of *Tell Me the Number Before Infinity: the story of a girl with a quirky mind, an eccentric family, and oh yes, a disability* (Many Names Press), and the author, editor, or co-editor of six books on women's issues. She is retired from careers in education and social work, and lives in Northern California. See: denataylorbooks.com

SUSAN TERRIS is a freelance editor, and the author of seven books of poetry, seventeen chapbooks, three artist's books, and two plays. Journals include *The Southern Review, Georgia Review, Prairie Schooner, Blackbird,* and *Ploughshares.* Poems of hers have appeared in *Pushcart Prize* and *Best American Poetry.* Her newest book is *Dream Fragments* (Swan Scythe Press Award). She is editor emerita of *Spillway Magazine* and a poetry editor at *Pedestal.* Her new poetry book *Green Leaves, Unseeing* will be published by Marsh Hawk Press, Spring 2024.
       website: susanterris.com

JUDITH TERZI is the author of *Museum of Rearranged Objects* (Kelsay) as well as of six chapbooks, including *Casbah* and *If You Spot Your Brother Floating By* (Kattywompus) and *Now, Somehow* (Finishing Line, 2022), poems about confronting a pandemic, cancer, and other health-related urgencies. Her poetry has appeared in a wide array of journals and anthologies and has been featured on BBC/Radio 3. She taught French for many years in Southern California as well as English at California State University, Los Angeles, and in Algiers, Algeria.
       Visit her website at: sharngtabouli.com.

ELLEN TREEN arrived in this world the day before the historic stock market crash in 1929. She grew up in the Midwest during the Great Depression, raised her children in the long shadow of the Cold War and the heat of the Civil Rights movement, and found her voice in the feminist era. Participating in and bearing witness to the political and cultural events of the 20th century informed every aspect of her life and writing. After frequent moves to various parts of the country, she found her way to California in the 1970s. Ellen Treen died at her home in Santa Cruz, weeks before her eighty-seventh birthday and the historic presidential election of 2016.

LYNDA WATSON was born in Orange, California. She did undergraduate work in Drawing and Illustration, Crafts and Jewelry, and received an M.A. and M.F.A. in Jewelry/Metalsmithing from California State University, Long Beach. In 1970 she was hired to build a Jewelry/Metals Program at Cabrillo College in Aptos, California, where she taught for 25 years. She was awarded two individual National Endowment for the Arts Fellowships and was named Santa Cruz Artist of the Year in 1998. In 2022, she was selected Master Metalsmith by the Metal Museum in Memphis, TN. Her work has been shown nationally and internationally, is in the permanent collections of museums here and abroad, and has appeared in numerous books and periodicals. A catalog of her work was recently published by the Metal Museum. She continues to make and show her work which is based on her life and travels.

BONNIE WEHLE serves as a docent at the University of Arizona Poetry Center and facilitates a monthly poetry circle with the county library. Her work appeared

in *Coal Hill Review, Rockvale Review, HerWords/Black Mountain Press, River Heron Review, Sky Islands Journal,* and elsewhere. Her chapbook, *A Certain Ache: Poems in Women's Voices,* was released by Finishing Line Press in 2022. Bonnie lives in Tucson, Arizona, with her dog, Tillie. Email: bonwehle@gmail.com
  Website: bonniewehle.com

FLORENCE WEINBERGER. Six times nominated for a Pushcart, once for Best of the Net, she has published six books of poetry, most recently *These Days of Simple Mooring,* winner of the Blue Light Press Book Award. Poems have appeared in journals including *Calyx, Rattle, Mantis, Miramar, River Styx, Ellipsis, Poet Lore, Comstock Review, Baltimore Review, Nimrod, Cider Press Review, Poetry East, Shenandoah,* and numerous anthologies.

MARY JO WERTHMAN WHITE is an Ohio poet and fiction writer. Her work has appeared in local and national journals, and on public radio station WYSO. In 2006, she was awarded the Paul Laurence Dunbar Poetry Prize. In 2012, she was the recipient of Antioch Writers' Workshop's Judson Jerome Poetry Prize and Scholarship. A poetry collection, *How the Universe Says Yes to Me,* was published in 2017 by Main Street Rag. Her debut novel, *An Invitation to the Party,* was published in 2023 by Regal House Publishing just in time for her eighty-first birthday. She is retired from Yellow Springs Schools and lives in Xenia, Ohio, with her husband and the good dog, Zaza.

KATHERINE J. WILLIAMS, art therapist and clinical psychologist, was director of the art therapy program at George Washington University where she is now associate professor emerita. Poems have been published in journals and anthologies such as *Poet Lore, Passenger, The Northern Virginia Review, 3rd Wednesday, Delmarva Review, The Widows' Handbook, How To Love the World: Poems of Gratitude and Hope,* and *The Wonder of Small Things, Poems of Peace and Renewal.* She recently published her poetry collection, *Still Life* (2022). One of her poems was nominated for a Pushcart Prize.
  Website: katherinejwilliamspoetry.com.

NELLIE WONG. Author of four books of poetry and with many poems and essays in numerous publications, Nellie Wong received PEN-Oakland's Reginald Lockett Lifetime Achievement Award in 2022. Her work has appeared in *This Bridge Called My Back: Writings by Radical Women of Color, The Iowa Review, Haight-Ashbury Journal, long shot,* and *Healing for a Fractured World,* among others. She is co-featured in the documentary film, "Mitsuye and Nellie: Asian American Poets." She performs with The Last Hoisan Poets and the Del Sol Quartet in the San Francisco Bay Area. Email: nelliewongpoet2@yahoo.com
Website: nelliewong.ddns.net

Previously Published Authors' Works

Angie Boissevain's "Losing Him," "Contemplating Work in Old Age," and "The Old Body" were previously published in *A Drum of Bone a Whistle of Silver,* Hummingbird Press, 2019. "Spine" and "Self Portrait at 80" were published in *The Healing Muse,* Fall 2017.

Wendy Taylor Carlisle's "Second Wave" was published in *Hags on Fire.*

Glenna Cook's "Shapes of Time" was published in *Shapes of Time,* MoonPath Press. "This Cannot Be" was published in *Thresholds,* MoonPath Press.

Alice Friman's "Hygiene" was published in *The Gettysburg Review* and "Painting the Wrinkles" in *I-70 Review.*

Maria Mazziotti Gillan's "First You Need to Lose Everything" was previously published in *VIA 2020–Voices in Italian Americana* (Bordighera Press).

Jan Harwood's "A Last Time" and "They" were published 3/3/22 in *Cultural Daily.*

Nancy Levinson's "Apologies At A Certain Age" appeared in *Hamilton Stone Review,* 2021.

Perie Longo's "Being Senior" was published in *Journal of Poetry Therapy,* March 2017, Vol. 30 #1.

Maude Meehan's poems are from *As If the World Made Sense,* Many Names Press.

Deena Metzger's "La Vieja" is from her novel *La Vieja—A Journal of Fire.*

Naomi Newman's "Old Ugly" was taken from her play *Snake Talk.*

Jean Nordhaus' "A Widow Reads Robinson Crusoe" has been previously published: online in Poetrymagazine.com and in *My Life in Hiding* (Quarterly Review of Literature Contemporary Poetry Series X).

Gunilla Norris' "The New Cord" was previously published in her book *Old and Singing,* Wayfarer Books, 2023.

Sylvia Pollock's previously published work: "Anniversary Song" *(Antiphon);* "Tourists" *(Risking It);* "Honeyed Days" *(Risking It).*

Bernice Rendrick's "Rubbings" was previously published in *Red Wheelbarrow,* 2010. "Pie Making" was previously published in *Monserrat Review.*

Mary Harwell Sayler's "Frontier" is from her book *A Gathering of Poems,* Independent Publishing.

Patricia L. Scruggs' "Degas' Bathers" was published in *Lummox Journal.*

Jan Seale's "A Woman's Body, Remembering" was first published in *Phoebe, Vol.* 16-1, Spring 2004. "Suddenly" was published in *Nape,* Ink Brush Press, 2011.

Myra Shapiro's "Put the Kettle On" first appeared in *Riverstyx Magazine.* "Dearth" and "Children When Autumn Comes" were first published in *Nimrod International Journal.*

Tilly Shaw's "Holding Hands" and "No Words for It" were published in *Swimming Closer to Shore,* Hummingbird Press, 2002.

Dena Taylor's "2020 Vision" was published in *Exclamation Points: Collected Poems,* Many Names Press, 2020.

Susan Terris' "To the Old Who Think They Want to Die" was published in *Persimmon Tree,* 2022

MJ Werthman White's "Let Me Tell You What It's Like" was previously published in the online journal, *The Vincent Brothers Review,* and in the poetry collection, *How the Universe Says Yes to Me,* Main Street Rag Publishing Company, 2017, page 17.

Katherine Williams' "Afterlife" appeared in her book *Still Life,* published by Cherry Grove Collections, 2022. "Old Woman Walking" was published in *Delmarva Review,* 3/2022.

Nellie Wong's "Silver on Ice" was previously published in *Giving Voice, LaborFest Writers Anthology* 2005-2017.

1

Recommended Reading & Resources

BOOKS

Eightysomethings: A Practical Guide to Letting Go, Aging Well, and Finding Unexpected Happiness, by Katharine Esty, PhD.
    What interviewees said: They are freer than they've ever been. It's okay to let go of some activities; just enjoy being. Don't fall!

Unexpectedly Eighty by Judith Viorst. Poems that will make you laugh.

Widow To Widow by Genevieve Ginsburg.
    Support, guidance, and insight for widows and others.

An Uncertain Age: Poems by Bold Women of a Certain Age. Anthology. Explores changing bodies, evolving priorities, what is held close, and what is left behind on the journey of aging.

Over 80: Reflections on Aging by Marilyn Reynolds. Silver Award Winner for Memoir, Northern California Publishers & Authors, 2022.

The Book of Old Ladies by Ruth Saxton. A celebration of women who push back against the limiting stereotypes regarding older women's possibilities.

The Well-Lived Life: A 102-Year-Old Doctor's Six Secrets to Health and Happiness at Every Age. In it, Gladys McGarey, M.D., who was a cofounder of the American Holistic Medical Association, outlines advice for others hoping to live—and enjoy—a long life.

Old Babes in the Wood. Stories by Margaret Atwood.

OTHER RESOURCES

There are several online blogs on being 80.
Google "blogs on being 80" and see what comes up.

Julia Louis-Dreyfus' "Wiser Than Me" podcasts.

AARP's "The Ethel."

Colophon

Many Names Press
believes in the power of published literature:
TO FOSTER RESPECT FOR WOMEN & CHILDREN EVERYWHERE,
TO OVERCOME INJUSTICE & WARRING MINDS,
TO DEVELOP WORK PARITY AND EQUALITY,
TO SUPPORT, NURTURE & PROTECT
THIS WORLD
FOR ALL BEINGS.

Robert Slimbach designed this digital postscript text type *Minion* in 1989. Its shape is based firstly on the lead typeface created by Nicolas Jenson in Mainz in 1470; then by Venetian printer & publisher Aldus Manutius with his punch-cutter, Francesco Griffo, in 1501; and finally after the Parisian Claude Garamond in 1545.

Minion has a legible and pleasant appeal, and is well suited for printing poetry because of its clean feet, well proportioned small caps and text figures.

MANY NAMES PRESS
MANYNAMESPRESS.COM

Printed in the USA
CPSIA information can be obtained
at www.ICGtesting.com
CBHW020007280624
10803CB00010B/256